RANDOM ESSAYS
ON MATHEMATICS, EDUCATION
AND COMPUTERS

JOHN G. KEMENY

Chairman, Mathematics Department
Dartmouth College

PRENTICE-HALL, INC.   Englewood Cliffs, N.J.

© 1964 by
PRENTICE-HALL, INC.
Englewood Cliffs, N.J.

Library of Congress Catalog Card Number 64-15212

Printed in the United States of America

To JEAN

whose random help was invaluable

PREFACE

Mathematics, education, and computers are three of the significant forces influencing our civilization. They have been the subject of wide-spread discussion. At various times I was called upon to write or talk on these topics, and in the present volumes I have tried to collect my thoughts on them.

Half the essays have appeared in print previously; in such popular publications as the *New York Times Magazine,* the *Atlantic Monthly,* and the *Nation,* in technical journals such as the *Mathematics Teacher* and *Daedelus,* and as parts of symposia published by the *MIT Press* and the *National Association of Secondary-School Principals.* (Acknowledgments will be found in footnotes.) Some others were written as lectures, whereas some are made public for the first time here.

These essays were written entirely at random. They have not been rewritten. No attempt was made to eliminate duplication or to develop a "great theme." Nevertheless, a number of shots fired at random may form an interesting pattern on the target. It is in this hope that the essays are here brought together.

JGK

CONTENTS

RANDOM ESSAYS
ON MATHEMATICS, EDUCATION
AND COMPUTERS

PART I MATHEMATICS

1 MATHEMATICS AND CULTURE

In the middle of the twentieth century, Man finds himself with few frontiers worthy of exploration on earth. His eyes have therefore turned towards the skies and inwards. Depending upon their temperaments, contemporary explorers reach for the stars or for the unexplored regions of the human mind.

Whether his travels carry him into space or into theoretical science, his passport must be stamped with the mathematician's seal of approval. We find that today mathematics is both one of the exciting frontiers to be explored, and the road to success in scientific and technological developments. Physics, chemistry, engineering, business, psychology, medicine, genetics, and dozens of other fields are conducting an increasing percentage of their work in this strange and potent language.

At the same time, most of the intellectuals in our country are almost wholly ignorant of the nature and promise of mathematics. Plato's Academy bore an inscription over its door forbidding entrance to the man ignorant of mathematics. Our twentieth-century university entrance requirements are not nearly so strict.

What is even more disturbing is the attitude of the average intellectual towards mathematics. He will be careful to profess knowledge and appreciation of literature, art, music, and other phases of the accepted culture, but he will boast of his ignorance of mathematics. Ignorance of the identity of Brahms, Renoir, or Voltaire would surely mean ostracism for the intellectual seeking cultural companions, but the names of Euler, or Gauss, or Cantor are likely to be unknown by those who set our cultural standards.

Let us now turn to our universities and examine their attitude towards mathematics. If the institution prides itself on a broad training program, it will usually demand a certain minimum knowledge of wide areas, typically listed as the humanities, the natural sciences, and the social sciences. Mathematics will be one means of fulfilling the often resented requirements in the natural sciences. These mathematics courses are usually taught as tools for the understanding of physics or engineering subjects—neither of which is pursued by the liberal arts student far enough to acquire any appreciation. Since the 12 years of school mathematics and the introductory college courses normally contain no mention of the mathematics of the last 150 years, the usual impression carried away by students is that mathematics is a necessary and boring evil for those unfortunate enough to need these dated tools for their research.

It is ironic that this impression persists in the era of greatest development in the history of mathematics. The number of papers published in mathematics doubled during the Forties, and doubled again during the Fifties. Entirely new branches of mathematics have developed during the last century, and many of these now rival the greatest achievements of ancient and medieval mathematics. At the same time that mathematics has taken on the widest possible importance in its applications, a vastly larger segment of mathematics is still pursued purely for its intellectual appeal.

It is a common impression that mathematics is cold and impersonal. It is true that it is impersonal, but no mathematician will admit that it is cold. Listen to one of the masters of mathematics:

> A mathematician, like a painter or a poet, is a maker of patterns. If his patterns are more permanent than theirs, it is because they are made with *ideas*. . . . A mathematician . . . has no material to work with but ideas, and so his patterns are likely to last longer. . . . The mathematician's patterns, like the painter's or the poet's, must be *beautiful;* the ideas, like the colours or the words, must fit together in a harmonious way. Beauty is the first test: there is no permanent place in the world for ugly mathematics.[*]

There is general feeling that application of mathematics to human affairs dehumanizes these affairs. Why is it all right to describe human behavior in English or Chinese, and particularly appropriate to describe it in French, but not in Mathematics? After all, they are simply varieties of man-made languages. The truth is that men hate to see wide use of a language they do not comprehend. As men all over the world resent it when a foreigner uses a language not known to them, there is universal resentment of the spread of the use of mathematics.

There is a strange mixture in attitudes towards the usefulness of mathematics. Men both overestimate and underestimate it. Most men feel that although mathematics is very useful in physics and engineering, it has no place in medicine, sociology, or business

[*] G. H. Hardy, *A Mathematician's Apology* (London: Cambridge University Press, 1940).

(other than business arithmetic). Yet there is no inherent reason why mathematics should, in the long run, be more useful in physics than in medicine. It is only that problems in medicine are more difficult to solve than in physics, and hence the use of mathematics will take a longer time to develop.

However, the same men are under the impression that the very act of formulating a problem as mathematics solves it. They have implicit faith in mathematical proofs of the existence of God, in quack formulas for winning at roulette, and in anything statistical.

It is time that we learned as part of our basic education that mathematics is simply a language, distinguished by its ability for clarity, and particularly well suited to develop logical arguments. The power of mathematics is no more and no less than the power of pure reason.

Any well-developed civilization suffers from a schism between intellectuals and nonintellectuals. The groups are divided by what they consider important in life, and there is no easy way of bridging a gap. Today we face the danger of an equally deep schism in the rank of the intellectuals, with knowledge of mathematics forming the impassable barrier.

Intellectuals look down upon those who cannot appreciate the higher things in life, whereas nonintellectuals try to cover their shortcomings by ridiculing intellectual pursuits. Today the same development threatens on a new level: that group of intellectuals which has mastered the secrets of mathematics is able to open up a new world of the mind, with an understanding of science and technology, and a chance to grasp the latest findings of modern research. They look down on intellectuals who are limited to the traditional disciplines. And the humanist tries to retaliate by disparaging scientific pursuits.

The cure for the first schism is widespread liberal education to qualify the masses for intellectual pursuits. The cure for the new schism is a totally new program of mathematical education. But, above all, the ultimate cure depends on a basic change of attitude, in which the majority (in each case) realizes that the minority has something fundamentally important to offer them.

2 EXPERIENCES OF A MATHEMATICAL MISSIONARY *

I traveled about 10,000 miles this year as a *visiting lecturer in mathematics*—or, as I prefer to think of it, as a *mathematical missionary*—for the Mathematical Association of America. I gave more than 100 lectures to about 10,000 people at two dozen colleges and universities, and spoke with representatives of many other schools. I ate countless pounds of roast beef, almost all of it far too well done. I found out how varied college cafeterias are: in some you get your silverware at the beginning of the line; in others, at the end.

Most of the institutions were in the western half of the Midwest. The list included small liberal arts colleges, denominational schools, teacher training institutions and large universities. On a typical day, I would give two lectures aimed primarily at undergraduates, either in large open meetings or in specially selected classes. I might then have lunch with members of the department and discuss problems of mathematical education. I would usually give an additional talk in the afternoon, which might be an expository mathematical talk or a talk on the various educational reforms we have instituted at Dartmouth College.

Throughout the day I would have discussions with individual members in the department or with students who had special problems that puzzled them. I frequently talked to groups of high school teachers and students as well. Usually at the end of a long day I had to pack up and catch a plane to my next stop. I traveled by train, plane, and rented car in order to make the grueling schedule possible in six and a half weeks. I was extremely fortunate that, although my trip was during the winter (half of it in December and half of it in March), I did not miss a single connection and was not forced to cancel a single talk.

Probably the most tiring part of the trip was the constant change. I slept in all kinds of hotels, motels, and dormitories. I

---

* Since this essay was written, in 1957, American education has moved in the directions here recommended. But it still has far to go.

even had the rare privilege of spending two nights in women's dormitories. My wife still does not quite believe the explanation that at these particular institutions the only guest suite available was at a women's dormitory.

I was grateful to Knox College in Galesburg, Illinois, for arranging a schedule that permitted me to spend five successive nights in the same hotel. I used Knox as my headquarters and, in addition to giving several talks to the excellent group of students there, I visited two neighboring institutions. This particular college proved to me that size bears no relation to the excellence of mathematical offerings. A highly enthusiastic and beloved chairman of a mathematics department can make up for whatever a department may lack in breadth or variety in its offerings.

My trip carried me into Canada for a single stop at the University of Alberta. While this was certainly one of my pleasantest visits, and I was most impressed by their mathematical educational program, it left me with one of my bitterest memories. Members of the Alberta faculty taunted me about United States mathematical education. I thought that I had almost won the argument when they pulled out a textbook from an American university in which the first two chapters were devoted to the teaching of the addition table and the multiplication table respectively. Ever since that day I have been trying to think of an adequate reply.

My trip got off to a very poor start. My first stop was scheduled at one of those newly created liberal arts colleges, which not too long ago were teachers' colleges, and in which the change had been mostly in name. To be perfectly frank, I had never heard of this particular institution before. I was met by a delegation of its mathematics teachers and we spent the first evening in informal discussion. I very quickly came to the conclusion that we had absolutely no interest in common, and that my trip to the institution would be completely wasted. I have never been more wrong in my entire life.

Three days later I left the college with the greatest possible respect for what they had achieved against insuperable odds. I had addressed over 1000 students in a series of carefully scheduled lectures, which assured that each student would have the opportunity to hear me speak several times on several different topics in mathematics. I found it impossible to walk down the campus without being cornered by students, who gave clear evidence of having discussed the contents of my lectures amongst themselves, and who simply· *had* to ask me one more question. If all colleges in the United States could develop the degree of enthusiasm for mathematics which was present on this one small campus during that particular week, I think that the supply of mathematically experienced men and women would far exceed the enormous demand.

Although most schools received me with most gratifying enthusiasm, this was not universally true. I was being accompanied to my first lecture on a certain campus by the chairman of the Mathematics Department. One of his students came up to him and asked: "Sir, where is the guest lecturer going to speak?" (Since I was a great deal younger than the student expected a mathematician to be and I did not have a long beard, it never occurred to him that I could be the guest lecturer.) The chairman turned to him and chastized him severely for wanting to go and listen to the guest lecturer, since the boy had an hour examination coming up the following day, and he persuaded the student to study for the exam instead. All of this took place in my presence.

Although the trip as a whole was certainly exhausting, it was not the tremendous number of lectures that tired me most. By nature I work best in the late evening. I therefore asked all schools to schedule my day between 10 a.m. and midnight. I would have thought that this was long enough to suit anyone's schedule. However, many schools decided that I must be joking in this matter, and not only did I not receive any invitations to speak after 10 p.m., but several times I was forced to speak at an hour of the morning when my brain could not function.

The most catastrophic example of this was in a fine small liberal arts college where I was asked to give five lectures in a single day, the first one of which was at 8 a.m. It happened to be a lecture I had given many times before. It was delivered in an overcrowded and an extremely stuffy room, and for the first time in my life, I fell asleep during my own lecture. Apparently I kept right on talking in my sleep, because when I woke up—perhaps ten minutes later—everyone seemed to be listening intently, but I had no idea whether I had covered a major topic or not. I decided it was safer not to go over it again, and started a new topic that had no relation at all to what I remembered saying previously. Fortunately no one in the audience noticed either the change of topic or the fact that I had had a pleasant nap.

I am not a heavy drinker by nature, but I do like an occasional drink, especially when I am very tired. This lecture-tour was certainly the driest period in my entire life. Some of the states I visited had laws against drinking alcohol, whereas other states—though having no such laws—seemed to consider it inappropriate to offer a mathematical visitor a drink. When I reached my final stop I was desperate for a cocktail. During the long and very beautiful drive from the airport to the university I could not resist asking my host whether the state I was in was a dry state. In reply I was told that the mean annual rainfall in the state was 14 inches, and then I was entertained for the rest of the trip with a detailed discussion of a variety of meteorological data.

The trip taught me even more than I was able to teach others. I came home firmly convinced that the time for reform in mathematical education is now.

Our curricula are cluttered with math courses that exist for no reason but force of habit; we teach them to our sons because we learned them from our fathers (who taught them to us only because they had learned them from their fathers, and so on back almost into prehistory). Whole units—a big slice of the traditional trigonometry course, for example—serve one, and only one, practical purpose: those who study them become qualified to teach them to others.

We have probably learned as much mathematics since 1800 as we did in all the years up to 1800. But it is a rare student who through grade school, high school, and his first two years of college hears even one mathematical idea less than 150 years old. Generally, this is because few of their high school teachers have heard of any, and few of their college teachers have bothered to insert any into their curriculum; but on my tour I found more than one college where no one on the faculty knew of a single mathematical development less than 100 years old.

This situation is the result of a number of factors, most of them related.

One is that the "educationists" have taken over our schools. Not that mathematical education was good before they did; after all, an idea that is 150 years old today was 100 years old 50 years ago. But the basic approach to education was different until about 1900. Until then, people went to school to learn, and the subjects they studied were considered fundamentally important, so a teacher was expected, above all else, to know his subject thoroughly. The educationists seem hardly to care what, if anything, a teacher knows about his subject; they care only that he teach "properly," using correct psychological techniques. So they pile on him one how-to-teach course after another, all but completely squeezing out of the curriculum the courses he should take—courses in his major subject. Even a prospective high school teacher often finds time in college for only 12 to 20 semester hours in his major. And some states allow a high school teacher to teach with only a single year of college work in his specialty. True, today's teacher is therefore unlikely to traumatize his students by using a "wrong" word. But he starts his teaching career hardly a step ahead of his students, and as knowledge in his field increases he is all too likely one day to find himself a step behind them.

This is especially serious as it concerns mathematics, because you can't really understand mathematics at any level until you have worked your way through one or two higher levels. And the situation is even worse in the grade schools than in the high schools and colleges. Many states will certify a teacher for all grades through the eighth without his having had even a *high school* math course. Make our children understand arithmetic, percentages and fractions, we tell this teacher—when he doesn't really understand them himself!

I happened to be present at one teacher training institution in the midst of a major fight with the State Board of Education. This particular college trained a large number of grade school teachers. Since all grade school teachers have to teach arithmetic as a significant fraction of their load, the college required of these teachers one semester course in the principles of arithmetic. Since for admission to this particular college only a year of high school mathematics was required, and this could easily be business arithmetic, the requirement meant that teachers would be allowed to teach arithmetic on all grade school levels without having had a single course beyond arithmetic. However, during this particular month there was a raging battle, started by the State Board of Education, trying to persuade the teachers' college to make the principles of arithmetic course optional rather than required of grade school teachers.

I was asked by the local staff to give them some sort of statement that could be used in their battle. I left them a statement that I believe that no one should be allowed to teach arithmetic unless he had one year of high school algebra. While they conceded the obvious desirability of this requirement, they pointed out the fact that this was completely utopian.

It was at the same institution that a few years earlier a survey was conducted to determine the changes in enrollments prior to the construction of a new building. The survey showed that whereas enrollments in most subjects were up, and that enrollments in mathematics and science were particularly rapidly rising, there was a single subject in which enrollments declined, namely, manual arts. This survey came as a great delight to the mathematics and science departments, who were hopelessly overcrowded and hoped that the new building was going to be a mathematics and science building. Perhaps it will come as no surprise to the reader that the new building was the most modern and beautiful manual arts building I have ever seen.

Of course, not only arithmetic, but also reading and writing have been greatly de-emphasized since 1900. Today's emphasis is on cooking, social adjustment and tap dancing.

And we have varsity sports. Of course we had these before 1900, too, but we view them a little differently now. For example: while I was at one Midwestern institution, an interviewer from the State Board of Education came looking for someone to fill a high school math vacancy. The department chairman offered him a list of excellently qualified seniors, but he would have none of them; he had already chosen his man, and hired him, though the chairman refused to recommend him. True, the man's record showed that he was totally unqualified to teach mathematics. But he happened to have been a football star, and the school in question needed a football coach, too.

I yield to no man in my enthusiasm for football. It is my favorite sport—spectator sport, that is—and I often use football problems and situations to illustrate my lectures. Yet this incident—which, I understand, is not unusual—shook me thoroughly. I am looking forward to hearing one day that some high school has hired a third-rate football coach just because he happened to be a first-rate math teacher.

During one of my stops the sole topic of conversation turned out to be the indictment of the president of the institution by the State Board of Regents. Apparently three students were caught in the act of committing grand larceny, had pleaded guilty, and were out on bail awaiting sentence. One of these three students was a star football player. I understand that the president of the university persuaded him to play a game while he was out on bail. This was but one of an endless number of stories I heard about various actions of this university president, making an intellectual atmosphere on the campus impossible. I am quite certain that this man is far from typical of the excellent group of men who devote their entire life to the running of a university. But it is frightening to think that this could happen in even a single reputable institution. I was delighted to hear later that he had been removed from his position.

But the fact that mathematical education is in a sorry state is one thing; the proposition that it ought to be improved is something else. Why take the trouble to improve it when it is so much easier to leave it as it is?

There are good reasons for taking this trouble. But before we list any of them, let us note that some have been promoting improvement for *bad* reasons.

We ought not seek improvement on the basis of either recent Russian scientific successes or the *immediate* value of mathematics in scientific research. Emphasis on immediate results, and promotion of mathematics as merely an international weapon, both violate the basic spirit of the scientific age. A country that won't undertake an experiment unless its fruits will appear within a limited number of years is unlikely to survive the scientific race. And the flaws in our educational system, which experts have pointed out for years, are flaws regardless of *Sputnik;* we should have been eager to eliminate them if we were the only country on earth.

We ought not justify mathematics on the basis of its very slight applications to everyday business problems; this is perhaps even more dangerous. I received a curriculum description recently from a high school that sends more than half its graduates to college; it noted, with properly concealed pride, that every single math course had been anchored to "practicality." This meant that discussions of business procedures took up much of the time supposedly devoted to mathematics during all four years. The very last twelfth-grade topic was a comparison of various types of insurance policies! Suppose the boy Einstein had been taught only such "practical" courses—who would have created the Theory of Relativity?

I was educated in Europe through the eighth grade, and thereby lost at least two years of how to read gas meters, and this loss may embarrass me seriously if I ever have to read one. But I have never had to read one yet. And the one time I had to read an electric meter I found that I could do so quite adequately despite my total lack of how-to-read-electric-meter courses.

Perhaps the most obvious *good* reason for improving mathematical education is that mathematics is the language of science. As such it will be indispensable to any future physical scientist or engineer, and its importance is growing steadily in the biological and social sciences. From this point of view, high school and the first two years of college are apprentice years for the prospective scientist. They give him nothing of direct practical value, but they *should* give him the material he must master to be able to understand the truly practical scientific subjects he will study later.

Even the boy or girl who will not be a scientist can profit from knowing this language, because we live in a scientific age more fully than most of us like to admit. Science isn't just the basis of our everyday life, the source of the necessities and luxuries we have grown so used to. It is also our principal intellectual stimulus. Therefore, no one is really educated unless he knows something about it.

However, mathematics can be justified on even better grounds. It provides a way of thinking and reasoning applicable to all fields; in fact, it *is* reasoning—in its purest form. The well-trained mathematician can solve all sorts of problems. I could cite case after case of mathematicians being called in as consultants on problems that had nothing to do with mathematics.

In short, mathematics develops the mind, and must be taught on this basis. As a mind developer—we must convince the high school student—it is more important than coed cooking, social adjustment, and tap dancing combined.

Then mathematical education should be improved. But how to improve it? I recommend:

1. *Throwing out much of what we teach today and replacing it with topics from modern mathematics.* These should be given in modest quantities in high school, in fairly large hunks during the first two years of college, and they should take up almost all of a math major's junior and senior years.

The junk to be thrown out comprises about a third of all the math taught in high school and the first two years of college, including many of the specialized computational techniques. I admit these help develop reasoning ability, but modern mathematics would do this every bit as well and *much* less wearisomely. Besides, most of the relics are sold not as reason developers, but as being "practically important," and whatever practical importance most of them had they lost a long time ago.

A considerable portion of my high school trigonometry course was devoted to the solution of oblique triangles. I pride myself on the fact that I was the best triangle solver my high school ever turned out. When I went to Princeton I found that I was up against very stiff competition. But whereas other freshmen might outdo me in many ways, I felt confident that I would shine when the time came to solve triangles. All through my undergraduate years I was waiting for that golden moment. Then I waited all through graduate school, through my work with Einstein, at Los Alamos, and while teaching and consulting for more than a dozen years. I have still not had an excuse for using my talents for solving oblique triangles.

If a professional mathematician never uses these dull techniques in a highly varied career, why must all high school students devote several weeks to the subject?

We find that a good deal of classical trigonometry is obsolete, that solid geometry could be condensed to a few topics in a plane geometry course, and that the approach to geometry and algebra must be modernized. Modern research in geometry and algebra has led to a basic understanding of these fields, and the inclusion of modern topics in these courses would go far towards increasing the students' interest. In addition, the student could profit by learning probability and statistics as well as being given a first introduction to such modern branches as logic, linear algebra, theory of games, topology, etc. College teachers commonly find that a student who was bored with traditional mathematics is fascinated with its modern counterpart. Our students should be introduced to these stimulating ideas at their most impressionable age, in high school.

2. *Upgrading mathematics teachers at all levels, but perhaps especially in the high schools.* Even the best educational system would be worthless without competent teachers to administer it.

But the job won't be easy. Three principal obstacles stand in its way.

Two of these we have already noted: that many of today's math teachers—including many who teach prospective math teachers—are pitifully out of date, and that increased emphasis on education courses has greatly reduced competence even in classical mathematics. The third obstacle is the tremendous teacher shortage. In many states, teachers are so scarce that 50 per cent or more of those teaching mathematics hold only "temporary certificates"—which means, generally, that they can't even meet the inadequate standards set up for regular teachers.

Actually, we have made some progress recently toward upgrading math teachers. The National Science Foundation has spent a lot of money financing various institutes for this purpose. Some of these, especially where competent lecturers have emphasized the significance of modern mathematics, have done a superb job, so that a fairly sizable number of teachers throughout the country have at least a nodding acquaintance with modern mathematical ideas. But a high school teacher, out of college perhaps 20 years, can learn only so much in one summer, so this type of program can be only a temporary expedient. It can't solve our basic problem.

Further, even while we are thus re-educating a small fraction of long-ago-graduated math teachers, our teachers' colleges are turning out every year a new crop, each even less well qualified than its predecessor. The time has come to face a fact: *the typical American teachers' college is unqualified to train mathematics teachers.* (And so, I learned on my trip, are many liberal arts colleges.)

I strongly recommend that the National Science Foundation establish a fellowship program, which might operate somewhat like the following.

A student who wants to teach mathematics, especially in high school, first takes three years, at any college, of liberal arts courses, elementary mathematics, and as much "education," heaven help us, as he must. He may then apply for a fellowship. If it is granted— in other words, if his first three years' record is good enough—he is sent to a college or university with an outstanding mathematics program, where during his fourth year, and perhaps a fifth, he gets a thorough, up-to-date professional mathematical education.

Would such a program cost a lot of money? Its cost would be negligible compared with the tremendous benefits we could derive from it. It could be supported for a whole year for much less than we pay for one jet bomber.

3. *Special sections for especially able students.* This is a very reasonable suggestion, but a number of times on my trip I almost got my head chewed off for it.

Students, let me stress, never resent such an arrangement. I have administered various types of honors programs, and always found the same reactions: those selected are happy to be among their peers, and the others are happy to be rid of those who could make them look bad by contrast.

School systems that have tried it have invariably reported the experiment a success. And why shouldn't it succeed? The idea of special sections for slow students, or students with special difficulties, seems to shock no one; is it less sensible to segregate bright students, also for their own good? Isn't it reasonable to give the college-bound high school student a college-preparatory curriculum, which is relatively a waste of time for anyone else? What does it cost anyone if a school that has to offer a course in three sections anyway makes one of the three an honors section?

But some do object, and with great vigor. One objecting group represents high schools too small to run parallel sections—too small even to separate college-bound students from those who want only to get out of high school as quickly as possible. From their point of view, I suppose, the objection is reasonable. But I submit that their point of view doesn't matter; schools of this size have outlived their usefulness. Ideally—and regardless of the outraged cries of localists who find community ignorance a small price to pay for having one's own basketball team—they must make arrangements whereby one school in an area offers only vocational training, another only a college-preparatory course.

Even more violently opposed are certain professional educators and politicians who find the idea *undemocratic!* This objection *must* be Communist-inspired. If we refuse to give our best brains all the education they can absorb, we virtually guarantee that Russia will win the Cold War—and this is exactly what these apostles of "democracy" are trying to persuade us to do.

4. *Prescribing a minimum high school curriculum for admission into college.* I feel such a curriculum must include four years of English, three years each of history, mathematics, science and a foreign language, and at least one year of elective work in a genuine academic field—say a fourth year of math for the science-oriented student, or additional work in languages for one who is arts-oriented. I think anyone who really wants to go to college should be willing to elect such a program. (I learned on my trip that hundreds of American high schools—especially small rural schools—don't even offer such a program.) I do not object, if a student has time, to his taking courses also in coed cooking, social adjustment, and tap dancing. But I think coed cooking and social adjustment are somewhat less important than English literature and American history, respectively, and I'm *sure* that tap dancing is an inadequate substitute for mathematics.

When I was new in the United States I greatly admired the system under which any student, regardless of his family or financial status, could attend a good college. But not until this year did I realize quite how far this privilege extends. American education is at a crisis; our colleges are tremendously overcrowded. Yet our state legislatures force them to admit thousands upon thousands of students who aren't qualified, who haven't the mental ability to profit from college, and who in four years of high school have shown not the least interest in studying. Of course, the vast majority of the unqualified never get past the freshman year; but even in so short a time they do a thorough job of watering down college for their able, interested fellows—and at state expense! Such a system, I submit, is idiotic.

A dean that I met has a very interesting theory. The major problem, he says, is not with the school that doesn't offer a college-preparatory course, but with the school that does offer one, but lists beside it a wide assortment of easy, colorful, inviting, nonacademic courses. Just as bad money drives out good, these easy courses drive out the hard ones, seducing even able students from the path of genuine education.

One student at his college had made an extraordinarily bad freshman record; the dean called for his high school transcript. On it he found unit after unit of the diploma-without-homework courses he expected to find, but fewer even of these than the state required for graduation. For a moment he was puzzled, then he noticed, at the bottom of the page—"Two units credit given for newspaper delivery." This story has come to symbolize for me the "modern" American educational system.

Colleges must both insist on higher standards in the high schools and be equipped to accommodate students with strong preparation. One incident typifies to my mind the terrific differences in the educational systems of good universities. I was told by the chairman of a Midwestern liberal arts college that his son had applied to the state university as well as to M.I.T. He was accepted by both institutions and elected to go to M.I.T., where he was placed in a course in the calculus and did very well in it. However, if he had gone to the state university, he would have been forced to take eight semester hours of mathematics before being allowed to elect the calculus. This waste of an entire year of a man's life certainly cannot be justified.

My preceding recommendations are rather general. On my trip I was often asked to recommend specific improvements for specific schools. Frequently this was hard to do.

For example, what could I tell the acting department head whose teaching load was more than twice as heavy as that of any *instructor* in my department—who had absolutely no secretarial help and had to grade all his own papers? I did try to point out to his president the handicap this department was working under, and was prepared to suggest that it be allocated a little more money, but the president pointedly changed the subject before I had a chance.

And what could I suggest to the chairman whose department was permitted to subscribe to only two mathematical journals and had only $50 a year for books? I hated to admit that at Dartmouth we get over 100 mathematical journals and our *monthly* book budget is more than twice $50. These people have problems that can't be solved without money.

But lack of money isn't the only difficulty. Perhaps even more formidable is the haughty refusal of many "experts" to believe that "ordinary people" can become interested in "difficult" subjects. And hand in hand with this obstacle goes another: an unfortunately large number of key people—though by no means all—are themselves basically uninterested in these subjects.

For example, although deans at a few of the schools I visited went to considerable trouble to attend my talks, and often contributed a great deal to the discussion, the vast majority felt they owed me only an apology for not attending. I have the most wonderful collection of deans' excuses. I shall always remember fondly the one who told me, very earnestly, how much he would have liked to hear my talk, but unfortunately the faculty lounge was about to be refurnished and he had to attend a meeting to discuss the color of the new upholstery. If its subject hadn't been so extremely important, he assured me, he would certainly have skipped this meeting to hear me.

At another school I gave four lectures over a day and a half. The president attended none of them, and I was introduced to him after the fourth, which I had given in midafternoon. He immediately apologized for the poor attendance I must have had; it was just terrible the way students weren't interested in mathematics "at an institution of our type," and besides, there had been all sorts of conflicting activities that afternoon. When he finished, the math chairman told him that the last lecture had drawn more than 150 students. The president looked thunderstruck; you could almost hear him wondering to himself whether the whole student body had gone mad.

A colleague of mine once listed for a group of mathematics teachers the basic courses Dartmouth offers prospective high school mathematics teachers. Did we ever manage to persuade anyone to take *all* these courses, one man asked. My colleague gently set him straight: "All these courses" were just *prerequisites* to the math major at Dartmouth, and many students take three times as many, and gladly.

I found on my trip that even radio announcers are "experts" in the sense that virtually everyone who interviewed me—a fairly sizable total—was scared to death that whatever I said would be far, far above the heads of my audiences. These "experts," I am convinced, are absolutely wrong.

One of my lectures, on modern algebra, was entitled, "Creation of a Branch of Mathematics." In the lecture I tried to show students how they themselves might have invented group theory, a fundamental branch of modern mathematics. To succeed, this lecture *had* to have active audience participation—which it *never* failed to get, even from high school students.

True, its unvarying success proved, I think, that mathematics, to be interesting, must be presented properly—but I think mathematics should be presented properly, anyway. My emphasis, in every lecture, was on trying to get across to my audience the fascination that modern mathematics holds for its practitioners. I also emphasized, again and again, that mathematics is growing and developing as rapidly as any science. I tried to ensure that every listener could picture modern mathematics as an area in which he, personally, might make a significant contribution. And this, I think, is the proper way to present mathematics.

My lecture on "Applications of Mathematics to the Social Sciences" seemed to succeed especially well with faculty groups. In this lecture I gave six entertaining examples of how six different branches of mathematics had been applied to six social sciences. The professors were usually fascinated—and no more, I think, by the story of *past* successes in this field (which have been fairly meager) than by the hope the talk presented of *future* successes.

In short, I found that most people at almost every level—except the level of dean—were interested, or willing to become interested, in mathematics. Students showed their interest in concrete ways. They stopped me on the street to question me about points I made in my lectures, and they pumped question after question at me when a lecture was finished. One group of high school students attended a lecture I gave primarily for a college audience; they hung around, asking questions, for an hour and a half after I was finished, until their teachers dragged them away almost by force.

Faculty members, whom I reached best at faculty luncheons, asked almost endless questions about educational experiments going on all over the country.

Even newspapermen and radio announcers—once they got over their fear that I couldn't bring myself down to the level of their audiences—were interested, and showed their interest by asking keen, penetrating, intelligent questions.

It is this widespread interest that convinces me that the job, though difficult, can be done. And it *must* be done. The goal must be to assure that every high school and college in the country— if not every grade school—has on its staff at least one competent, enthusiastic modern mathematician, able not only to teach mathematics but also to encourage able young people to make their careers in it.

Near the end of what was a most instructive and fruitful, but extremely tiring, venture it became clear that I would need a lengthy rest to recuperate. This was particularly true since I seemed to be running a fever during the last few days. Hence, I had to prescribe three days of rest for myself upon returning to Dartmouth College. As it turned out, I was in for a considerably longer rest, since my slight cold turned out to be virus pneumonia, and I spent the next five weeks in bed.

3 MATHEMATICS INVADES THE
SOCIAL SCIENCES *

Before coming here, I heard that many of you shared a common experience this summer, in reading three books on science. I decided to share this experience with you—and it turned out to be most pleasant since the books were excellent selections.

I am particularly pleased that many of you have read *Can Science Save Us,*† since this book presents an unusually strong case for the inevitable growth of the social sciences. It presents cogent arguments why the sciences must grow; it makes a persuasive case that this growth is possible, and it answers a number of stock objections. I shall therefore take it for granted that you are by now convinced that within your lifetime the social sciences will reach a new level of respectability.

But there is one major objection to this book: the author almost completely ignores the role that mathematics must play in these developments. Indeed, this seems to be a common failing of men writing about science. Even so distinguished an author as James B. Conant barely finds room for a mention of mathematics in his *Science and Common Sense.*‡ I am left with the impression that this world famous scientist and educator has failed to appreciate the critical role played by mathematics throughout the history of science.

The most often discussed example of the interaction between mathematics and science is the dual role played by Newton. In reading his biography, one visualizes him as a brilliant young physicist asking a number of fascinating questions that neither he nor anyone else can answer. Newton comes to the conclusion that there are some new mathematical tools needed before he can progress. So he puts aside his physics thinking hat, and puts on the

---

* James Bowdoin Day Lecture, October 12, 1962.
† George A. Lundberg, *Can Science Save Us* (New York: David McKay Co., Inc., 1961).
‡ James B. Conant, *Science and Common Sense* (New Haven: Yale University Press, 1951).

hat of a mathematician for several years. In this new role he invents Calculus. Then he again changes hats, and the world of physics reaps the fruits of these powerful new mathematical methods.

An even more interesting example was told to me by Albert Einstein. For his Special Theory of Relativity the mathematics of the early 1900's was entirely adequate. But when he came to the General Theory, he needed new means of studying non-Euclidean geometries, and Einstein began to develop a new branch of mathematics. Very fortunately, a friend of his heard about this, and told Einstein that a little-known Italian mathematician had just recently invented precisely the kind of mathematics that Einstein was groping for. Here the mathematician had the tools ready for the physicist—just in the nick of time.

As a last example, consider the development of genetics. Mendel made his pioneering discoveries just 100 years ago. Of course, genetics has grown as a science tremendously since that time, but it is within the last generation that entirely new doors were opened for it. The reason is that genetics had to await the advent of modern probability theory.

Each science passes through an early stage, where the emphasis is on experimentation. This is usually followed by attempts to generalize and arrive at qualitative theories. These are the stages discussed in Conant's book. But the sciences that have truly affected man's life have passed through these stages, to the stage of the abstract mathematical theory.

Why should mathematics play such a key role in science? To answer this question we must consider the nature of mathematics. Our modern view of mathematics is that it is precise, systematic, abstract reasoning, and all abstract reasoning that is sufficiently precise and systematic constitutes mathematics. Therefore, my assertion that advanced science requires mathematics is merely a modest statement that science in its later phases must think precise, systematic, abstract thoughts.

Let us now turn to the social sciences. If one examines subjects like economics, psychology, sociology, or political science, one finds a few examples that are without doubt science, and a vast array of discussions that are completely unscientific. Since we have agreed to grant that scientific social science is a possibility, should we perhaps blame the practitioners of some of these pseudosciences? It is my opinion that this is not a reasonable analysis of the difficulty.

My own view is that we are witnessing the dawn of some new

sciences. It is easy to point to the recent triumphs of modern physics. But let us examine what physicists were writing 2000 years ago, and we would agree that most of it ranged from the unscientific to the absurd. It is also most disturbing to note that the leading intellectuals of the age often ignored the scientific and praised the absurd.

Perhaps, if anyone is to blame, we, the citizens of a very impatient democracy, should be called to answer for the troubles of the social sciences. An economist comes to us and offers to predict the trend in savings accounts in Brunswick, Maine. Instead we ask him to predict the entire trend of the American economy for the next decade. A psychologist is prepared to offer a means of improving one person's rate of learning by five per cent. Instead we ask him for a single test that will predict the best future profession of any six year old. Or a sociologist may offer to make some modest predictions of how a given group of five men will react to a puzzling situation, and we ask him instead to give a complete analysis of personal interactions in the United Nations.

Kepler's three laws of planetary motion were wonderful discoveries. But what if he had been pressured to abandon this research in favor of designing a space ship? What if Mendel had been denied his garden peas and asked to work on a study of human heredity? Or what if Madame Curie had been told that her work was worthless unless she invented an atomic bomb? These distinguished scientists would certainly have failed in these impossible tasks, and might never have made their greatest discoveries.

Let us therefore encourage the social scientist to work on problems in which he has hope of succeeding, and let us wait another century or two and the progress of the social sciences will revolutionize human life.

But can we find any evidence, no matter how modest, which will support the claim that the effect of mathematics is beginning to be felt in these new areas? I believe that there is ample evidence. But the evidence may not be convincing to the layman.

Suppose that 2000 years ago you had the task of convincing an intelligent but skeptical listener that the day of mathematical laws in physics was approaching. Probably the most clearcut example you could have produced would have been Archimedes' Law of the Lever. This says that one can lift a weight x times as heavy by applying leverage to a lever x times as long. Of course, this has practical applications, but qualitatively these applications must have been well known. Farmers must have known thousands of years before that a heavy stone can be dislodged by using a long and strong stick as a lever, and they must also have been aware that the heavier the stone, the longer the necessary leverage.

What did Archimedes contribute to this? Merely that he put the relationship into precise mathematical form: with twice the length of stick you can lift twice as heavy a stone, with three times the length you can balance three times as heavy a weight, etc. But would your skeptical friend of 2000 years ago not be justified in responding "so what?" It is only in retrospect that we realize that Archimedes was one of the pioneers of mathematical physics. Even Archimedes did not dream of the fantastic progress of the last two millennia. So let us be cautioned, and look for modest, simple laws which seem to work well within a limited framework.

It is easiest to find convincing examples in economics. Since much of this subject matter can be discussed in monetary terms, it is natural to look for mathematical relations. No doubt the most spectacular success in recent years has been in developing an entirely new branch of mathematics, known as linear programming. It serves to compute (in fairly simple circumstances) the means of achieving the largest possible profit, or minimizing one's expenditures. Where the theory is applicable, it both finds the best possible solution, and it provides a proof that no better solution is possible.

From psychology I shall cite learning theory. This branch originated with observations of how lower animals learn to perform simple tasks. The early successes were derived from long and patient experiments with rats and pigeons. But more recently some modest advances have been made in simple human experiments. For example, a theory has been developed as to how fast humans memorize a list of new words. This example is interesting in that the mathematical theory required is a branch of probability theory in which much current mathematical research is still carried on.

It is harder to find good examples in sociology or political science, presumably because human interactions are a very difficult and complex subject. Some of the nicest applications of mathematics to these areas have been the applications of some abstract, non-numerical branches of modern mathematics. For example, the theory of graphs is beginning to play a key role in the study of social organization.

It is particularly notable that all three of these examples involve mathematics developed during the last generation. Perhaps this is not a fair sample, since I happen to be interested mostly in modern mathematics. But most mathematicians who have attempted work in the social sciences have come to the conclusion that even newer methods have to be developed before the social sciences can hope to rival the older branches of science.

I have tried to point out, earlier, that there is a fascinating interaction between science and mathematics. Sometimes the need of the scientist leads to new mathematical discoveries, as in the case of Newton. Sometimes the mathematics is invented first, as in the case of the theory of relativity. And sometimes independent discoveries in mathematics and science reinforce each other—an event that we are now witnessing in the applications of modern probability theory to genetics. It, therefore, seems reasonable to expect that progress in the social sciences will have to be matched by still further strides in the expansion of the realm of mathematics. I fully expect that within the next century the social sciences will serve as the major source of new problems to stimulate the mathematician's creative imagination.

Let me conclude this address on a more personal note. All of you must at one time or another have wondered what contribution you can make to the progress of civilization. You may be disturbed by the many articles and books that claim that the trouble with our civilization is that there are no frontiers left to explore.

Indeed, there are perhaps only two opportunities for you to explore new frontiers: you can join the Peace Corps, or you can train to become an astronaut. In the Peace Corps you can help to explore some little known areas of the world, and bring young nations into the family of civilized countries. As an astronaut you might get a chance to explore the further reaches of the solar system. Both of these professions have very few openings, and require a very unusual type of person.

But as our physical frontiers shrink, the frontiers of the mind are ever expanding. There is truth in the old saying that the more we know the more we realize our ignorance. It is certainly true that the number of unanswered questions increases in each generation. As we answer a few old problems, we learn to ask new, more difficult questions for the next generation to puzzle over. So that if you have the blood of the pioneers in you, I strongly urge you to acquaint yourself with the immense frontiers of the searching human mind.

I do not wish to suggest that any one frontier should be pursued to the exclusion of all others, but I have tried to call your attention to the newest territory about to be opened—a territory that might otherwise not have come to your attention. There is a great need for mathematically trained men in a wide variety of fields, starting from pure mathematical research, through the traditional sciences, to engineering and the huge field of computing machines. But I believe that the greatest opportunity for a significant contribution at the moment lies in the expert mathematician who is willing to devote his life to the exploration of a social science.

The hundredth anniversary of the last covered wagon is approaching. Let us pay tribute to our ancestors who had the courage to set out west in a covered wagon, with some simple farm implements for equipment, and with the inevitable shotgun for protection. But if you want to follow in their footsteps I would suggest that in place of a covered wagon you acquire a well-rounded liberal education, in place of farm implements you equip yourself with an insatiable interest in human problems, and in place of the shotgun you would be well advised to arm yourself with the weapons of modern mathematics.

4 TEACHING THE NEW MATHEMATICS *

While mathematics has always been recognized as one of the corner-stones of our educational system, we are entering an era in which an understanding of mathematics will be of even greater importance to all educated men. As our civilization grows in complexity and science plays a more and more vital role, the man ignorant of mathematics will be increasingly limited in his grasp of the main forces of civilization.

Within a single lifetime a dozen major new areas have been opened in mathematics, and today mathematics is one of the most rapidly growing fields of human knowledge. But new discoveries often take several generations to reach the level where the majority of educated people hear of them.

The first definitive book on mathematical logic was written in 1910 by Bertrand Russell and A. N. Whitehead. In the Twenties we find a handful of pioneers, destined to become world-famous, proving the fundamental theorems of the subject. These same pioneers trained the first group of disciples in the Thirties, making it possible for a small number of universities to offer graduate courses in mathematical logic. These disciples turned out a large number of students after World War II. Today a fourth generation of mathematical logicians is teaching the subject on a broad scale in our colleges.

Modern mathematics is impossible to define in terms of its subject matter. The new mathematics is typified by its approach. Whenever a mathematician observes a pattern in nature, he immediately asks, "What are the essential features of this pattern?" Then he asks what one can deduce from these features. At this stage he forgets all about the example that motivated his research and considers the problem in its pure, abstract form. The advantage of this approach is that his results will have far-reaching applications. Every pattern that shares the given features will also have to share whatever additional features the mathematician has inferred.

* First appeared in *The Atlantic Monthly*, October 1962. Reprinted by permission of *The Atlantic Monthly*.

During this period in which mathematics is growing and maturing in its basic research, entirely new demands are being made on the world of mathematics. The biological and social sciences are beginning to vie with physical sciences for the services of mathematicians. Many research papers in medicine, psychology, and economics are unreadable for the mathematically uninitiated.

Ideas invented out of intellectual curiosity often turn out to have far-reaching practical applications. The study of geometries of more than three dimensions may at first appear impractical. But relativity theory now requires four dimensions, of a non-Euclidian type. Modern economic theory may employ an abstract geometry of a hundred dimensions to describe the interaction of a hundred different industries. Quantum mechanics has made use of infinite-dimensional geometries. But these applications, while certainly profiting from the new mathematics, have nowhere the abstraction with which the topologist views geometry. We may be assured that when science is ready to make demands for a more basic understanding of geometries, the field of topology will provide answers.

Large industries are now interested in hiring a staff of mathematicians to help in their planning. In some cases this is due to the development of branches of mathematics specially suited for long-range planning, such as linear programming and the theory of games. But even more important is the realization that the man with mathematical training is often best qualified to solve problems of almost any type.

A staff of mathematicians may now solve accurately a scheduling problem that was solved by hit-or-miss methods before. A statistician may find a way to improve the quality of a product, and at the same time lower the cost of supervision. A mathematical logician may be in charge of designing electric circuits. And a telephone company may find it profitable to have a large staff of abstract mathematicians on hand. We even find mathematicians working on military strategy.

All of these demands on the mathematician are modest compared with the requirements of computing machines. With hundreds of these giant brains manufactured annually, there is a danger that mathematicians may have to spend all their time instructing the machines. For example, a single installation of the U.S. Navy advertised for 5 Ph.D.'s, 10 M.A.'s, and 25 B.A.'s for a computing center. The request sounds perfectly reasonable until one realizes that—based on the average output of the last decade—the Navy is proposing to hire 0.5 per cent of the B.A.'s, 1 per cent of the

M.A.'s, and 2 per cent of the mathematics Ph.D.'s graduated in a year throughout the entire country!

During a period of revolutionary change, men need the comfort of something unchangeable and hallowed by tradition. Apparently, the undergraduate curriculum has fulfilled this need for mathematicians. I can think of no other reason for the fact that many leaders of mathematical research teach the same dull, unenlightening, and completely outdated topics year after year. Of course, the staffs at the majority of institutions of higher learning have little choice; they teach what they know. Since their own professors had neglected to bring them into contact with present-day developments, they could hardly be expected to go back to graduate school late in their careers. Nor is it reasonable to expect a man in his fifties to turn his advanced students over to a youngster with a fresh degree. The most human reaction is to decide that the newer mathematics is not worth teaching.

But the pressure of future employers, of the engineering schools, and even of the new men in the social- and biological-science departments is having its effect. More and more mathematics departments have decided that they must change the curriculum, whether they are ready to teach the new subjects or not.

If adopting new courses is difficult, designing a new curriculum from scratch is incomparably harder. A college needs experts in a variety of mathematical branches (no small group could hope to speak for all of mathematics), all willing to participate in a time-consuming experimental program. Even if such a group existed, it is unlikely that its efforts would be unhampered by the rest of the department or the administration. Vested interests are as strong inside ivy-covered walls as outside, and they seem to last longer in the protected atmosphere.

Happily, a strange series of circumstances produced just the right combination of factors at Dartmouth College. After 30 years of continuous service, almost the entire mathematics department was ready to retire, and the college decided to bring in a young Ph.D. to take charge of planning for the future. And so I came to Dartmouth in 1953, at age 27, to take part in the rebuilding program. Today we have 17 Ph.D.'s, three of whom have devoted over 30 years of their lives to Dartmouth, and the rest of whom have come since my appointment. We have been extremely fortunate in the caliber of the young men attracted to Dartmouth. In part they were drawn by the reputation of the college, in part by the youth of their colleagues (the median age dropped 30 years), but mostly by the opportunity of building a department and a curriculum to fit their own dreams. We have also had the encouragement and support of the senior members and of an enlightened administration.

Since it is easier to describe one program than to try to speak of national trends, I will concentrate on the Dartmouth mathematics program. I do not say that it is the best in the nation, but we have worked on it very hard. We do not claim to have invented all the ideas—indeed, we are indebted for them to a long list of mathematicians—but we have tried to combine the best of their ideas with some innovations of our own. At least our program points in the right direction, and many colleges and universities have paid us the great compliment of copying parts of it.

Our basic assumption is that no one or two programs can fill the needs of all students of mathematics. We have, therefore, designed four programs. We offer an honors major for the student aiming for graduate work in mathematics, and a major for the students who will make mathematics their career, but will do little or no graduate work. Included in this group are prospective high school teachers, computer programmers, and industrial mathematicians. We also provide a strong program for physicists and engineers, and we try to meet the ever-increasing needs of biological and social scientists.

Let me start with the last program, since this is entirely new in college curricula. In the past, the social-science student brave enough to elect mathematics in college soon found out that most of the mathematics he needed was attainable only among the courses reserved for mathematics majors, and that he was forced to wade through a morass of courses designed exclusively for engineers. We had to face up to the fact that almighty calculus is not nearly as important in the social sciences as in the physical sciences. Indeed, it may not even be as important in the physical sciences as the curriculum would lead us to believe. While all students should know some calculus, if they have but one year to imbibe, they should also taste mathematics of a different vintage. That is why we developed a course called Finite Mathematics, to supplement an introduction to the calculus.

The history of this course is most interesting. When we asked social scientists what mathematics other than calculus they use, they mentioned topics that were never taught below the junior year and often were reserved for graduate courses. We were certainly worried about teaching high-level mathematics to liberal-arts freshmen, but decided that it was better to fail to get across the material they needed than to succeed in teaching them something useless. Therefore, we chose some mathematical logic, probability theory, and linear algebra as our basic material, and for further study such ultramodern topics as linear programming, game theory, and Markov chains. But how were we to teach freshmen what some of our Ph.D.'s did not know?

The very nature of our subject matter came to our rescue. Since abstract mathematics develops from simple concrete examples, we found it possible to illustrate all the basic concepts in terms of familiar examples. We relied on the student's intuition, which is usually sound in the finite case but often misleads him when he is forced to contemplate infinity.

For example, in probability theory all questions concerning the outcome of an election are finite questions, in the sense that all possible variations are finite in number. But in picking a point on a line by some random device, we must allow infinitely many possibilities. The predictability of elections can be discussed in our freshman course; the picking of a point on a line cannot. I do not consider this a major loss for the students.

The course in finite mathematics was an immediate success at Dartmouth and has been a major factor in the decision of 95 per cent of all freshmen to study mathematics in college. It, and other courses similar to it, has been widely adopted throughout the country. But I did not fully realize how well we had succeeded until I overheard one of our freshmen telling his parents about the "fascinating new mathematics course, which has no mathematics in it at all." Indeed, the course had nothing in it that fitted his high school conception of the nature of mathematics.

Students interested in mathematics or in the physical sciences need a firm foundation in classical mathematics, though not necessarily an old-fashioned calculus course or three years of nothing but calculus. We not only have shortened the calculus sequence, but also have made it more interesting, we hope. We examined all the traditional topics to see whether there was a reason for including them, other than that they have always been taught. Second, we decided to spend more effort on teaching fundamental ideas and less on specialized skills. This decision has created the most controversy.

While mathematicians are willing to admit that many of the techniques taught to all students in the traditional curriculum have ceased to be interesting, it seems to us that few educators face up to the fact that the remaining techniques are likely to suffer the same fate. For example, we think that our engineering students are being given just the right training for the previous generation of engineers. Often, after taking jobs, they have to be retrained completely.

It is a common complaint that our students do not remember their freshmen skills by the time they need them in their junior year. Since many of these techniques are so complicated that the instructor himself must refresh his memory annually, the student can hardly be blamed. However, the instructor knows his basic principles so well that he can pick up the special tricks in a short time. If entirely new techniques are developed, he does not have to start from scratch; he simply reads an account of the new developments.

The educational implications are clear. Let us teach our students only basic ideas and fundamental techniques. Let us teach them to use reference materials and to read the current literature. They may still need on-the-job training or periodic retraining, but they can do most of this for themselves. They will not feel that the bulk of their college education was wasted.

One must also take into account the impact of computing machines. Often we train our students to become second-rate computing machines. This may have had some use 30 years ago, but today we cannot possibly compete with electronic computers. Let us leave to the machines all that is dull and purely mechanical and turn our efforts to more enjoyable tasks.

Physical scientists need the modern tools too. We teach a more advanced version of the finite mathematics course to all of them in their sophomore year and have them ready for advanced courses by their junior year. We offer a selection of courses designed to introduce them to any field in mathematics, pure or applied.

The best testimonial for this program is the success of some of our weakest students in their future careers. They may have felt while at Dartmouth that they were lagging behind their classmates, but later they found that their training put them ahead of graduates of classical curricula.

I hope that I have conveyed our deep interest in students of all types. But I should be less than honest if I did not admit that the primary educational aim of any mathematician is the training of mathematicians. The honors program has always been our special concern. In no field is the difference between the best students and very good students as great as in mathematics. There is that special gift for mathematics which, though it can be cultivated, can only be provided by nature. The greatest crime of the traditional curriculum, from kindergarten through college, is the neglect of the exceptional student of mathematics. I am quite certain that many more men and women have left mathematics because of boredom than because of the inability to comprehend.

I have followed many fine experiments in ability grouping in grade and high schools and have not been surprised by the amazing success of some of these programs. On the college level, the cure was introduced by Princeton University, and we have tried to follow that outstanding example. The mathematically promising student must be located as soon as he arrives on the campus, must be allowed to study within small groups, among his peers, taught by research mathematicians.

While I have laid great stress on good curricula for other students, for honor students the subject matter is almost irrelevant. These students may be recognized by their attitude towards the material that is not in the syllabus. When an average class is told that they are about to treat a topic that will not appear in the final exam, they take this as a signal to catch up on their sleep. Honors sections come to life when they are allowed to wander freely into topics that are not required.

Since these students can cover the required material with much less drill, there is time for mathematical excursions of the mind. They are encouraged to work out as much mathematics as they can for themselves and to ask the instructors anything at all, as long as it concerns mathematics. We know that in spite of this "wasted time," they will acquire a much deeper understanding of basic mathematics, and we cultivate their taste for more esoteric material by responding to their own requests. I particularly enjoy teaching a freshman honors section. In a single year I may be forced to tell them about the fourth dimension, infinity, some theorem in topology that has caught their imagination, or just what a mathematician does when he creates.

Since the first two years of the honors program are open to any able student who loves mathematics, it is not uncommon to find a future doctor, lawyer, businessman, or musician studying side by side with the budding mathematician. But we try to identify the latter by his junior year, and then he is allowed to progress at his own speed. He has the opportunity of covering the equivalent of a strong master's program as an undergraduate. He is exposed to courses in modern versions of the calculus, algebra, and geometry, as well as topology, probability theory, logic, number theory, and applied mathematical fields. As far as possible, honors majors study in seminars, and they are encouraged to explore mathematics on their own.

We are particularly proud of having pioneered in the wide use of undergraduates as research assistants. Perhaps they cannot do as much as advanced graduate students, but mathematics is a field for the young in mind. Our computing center is staffed exclusively with undergraduate assistants; others are assigned to individual faculty members to help them on research projects. Though this may mean simply the checking of computations, or reading of manuscripts, or searching in literature, many assistants have also contributed original ideas to faculty research, and so far three of our assistants have published original papers of their own.

As these students, and students from other institutions, reach our graduate schools, we hope to provide the staff necessary to spread modern mathematical ideas to all colleges. The potential of mathematics may have been dormant, but our colleges are awakening. The next generation will have a chance to become mathematically literate.

5 RIGOR VS. INTUITION
IN MATHEMATICS *

I thought that I might make some informal remarks this evening about the role of rigor and the role of intuition in both mathematical research and in the teaching of mathematics. The best way to contrast these two very important trends is by a story told about one of our leading graduate schools. There was an advanced seminar in topology in which the lecturer devoted the entire hour to writing out a proof with complete rigor. After having filled all the blackboards, he had everyone in the room completely lost, including one of his own colleagues, who jumped up and said, "Look, I just don't understand this proof at all. I tried to follow you, but I got lost somewhere. I just didn't get it at all." The lecturer stopped for a moment, looked at him, and said, "Oh, didn't you see it? You see, it's just that the two spaces connect like this," intertwining his two arms in a picturesque fashion. And then his colleague exclaimed, "Oh, now I get the whole proof."

There is something in this story that is typical of a great deal of mathematical research. You can write down long formulas to make a proof complete and rigorous. Indeed, you *have* to write down long formulas and justify every step. Yet very often there is one key idea which, once understood, makes the rest of it purely routine. And if this one idea is not understood, the whole proof is meaningless to the student or to the research worker.

My basic theme this evening is that I am somewhat worried that amongst all the very fine reforms that are being suggested, tried out, and patiently worked out on the high school level, there may have come an overemphasis on rigor and a playing down of intuition in mathematics. This evening I am going to try to plug for continued emphasis on the role of intuition in the teaching of mathematics.

If you look at the problem historically, you will find that rigor

* Banquet address, National Council of Teachers of Mathematics, Salt Lake City, August 23, 1960. Printed in *The Mathematics Teacher*, February 1961. Reprinted by permission of *The Mathematics Teacher*.

always enters mathematics quite late. Euclidean geometry is identified as one of the high points in mathematical rigor. Yet Euclid is full of holes from any modern standpoint. A great deal of publicity has been given to this, and I won't dwell on it. Let us take only one small point. It is impossible to prove from Euclid's axioms that a circle has an inside and an outside. Of course, it is quite important to know that a circle has an inside and an outside; however, since this proof requires a considerable effort in an advanced graduate course in mathematics, it was perhaps fortunate that Euclid didn't realize that he couldn't prove this. In the last analysis he knew very well that a circle does have an inside and does have an outside. This does not mean that the Jordan Curve Theorem is not of importance to modern mathematics. It is tremendously important, but the fact that this major hole exists in Euclidean geometry does not destroy the value of Euclid's work.

Let me jump over several centuries to Newton's work on the calculus. If any of our freshman students in calculus should perform in the sloppy, unjustifiable way in which Newton did the calculus, we would surely refuse to pass him. Nevertheless, I would like to maintain that Newton's work was, in the long run, quite valuable.

I come to one of the greatest names in the history of mathematics, that of Euler. Euler was quite capable of doing rigorous mathematics, but occasionally he did hair-raising things. His manipulation of some infinite series, for example, was completely unjustifiable. As a matter of fact, it took the next two hundred years of mathematical progress to find out that practically everything that Euler did could be justified, though there was no real reason why Euler should have suspected this. Euler was just "plain lucky"— with dozens of major ideas, almost every one of which turned out to be right. His remarkable mathematical intuition has never been equaled.

The following story is told about a very famous modern mathematician, one of the co-founders of a great branch of mathematics. He had published a certain paper in which he mentioned a theorem without proof, and a Russian mathematician wrote to him, asking whether it would be possible to receive a proof. Our distinguished mathematician answered the Russian request. After about a month or so he had a reply. The Russian mathematician thanked him profusely; however, he had to point out that the proof sent was for a completely different theorem and that the proof was incorrect. As a matter of fact, this particular mathematician is credited with many incorrect proofs, and yet there isn't a single creative mathematician who would not list him as one of the greatest mathematicians of the century.

After this very elaborate historical introduction, I want to ask you a simple question. If it is possible for Euclid, for Newton, for Euler, and for many contemporary mathematicians to go down in history as among the great, even though they were far from completely rigorous, don't you think that the same sin might be forgivable on the part of high school students?

Let me be more specific. Let us talk a little about definitions. Everybody knows that one has to be very rigorous in definitions. There has been a strong trend in recent years to make modern concepts—like that of a function—exceedingly rigorous. I was particularly pleased that in this trend, set theory has played a major role. It so happens that I wrote my Ph.D. thesis on set theory, and therefore I am exceedingly fond of it. Perhaps I may perform a public service by seeing to it that, as long as we define functions in terms of sets, we make sure that the definition is really rigorous.

You all know that a function, when correctly defined, is a set of ordered pairs. Of course, people don't quite take the trouble to distinguish between an ordered pair and an unordered pair. There happens to be a very nice way of doing this. It is the standard method in set theory: to get an ordered pair in set theory (which deals with unordered sets), you just define an ordered pair as a set having two sets as elements. For example, if you want the ordered pair $\langle A, B \rangle$, one of the elements is the pair $\{A, B\}$ and the other element is a set whose only element is A. Now you can identify which is which, because A belongs to both of these and B only to one of them. Then you've got something that will serve as an ordered pair.

The mathematical logician would then define a function as follows: "A function is a set of sets of sets, such that each element is a two-element set consisting of a one-element set and a two-element set, and the one-element set is a subset of the two-element set. Furthermore, for each object whose unit set is an element of an element of the function, there is at most one other object which is an element of one of the elements of the elements of the function to which the given object belongs." I am delighted that this kind of highly enlightening and intuitive material has finally reached the high school level. We couldn't dream of teaching it to undergraduates in college, but I am delighted to see that you are teaching this material in high school.

My point obviously is that there *must* be a more intuitive way of defining a function. This is a particularly amusing example to a logician who happens to know the history of this particular subject. Around the turn of the century, for the first time, mathematicians interested in the foundations of mathematics developed two fundamentally different approaches to the foundations of mathematics. In one of them, pioneered by Zermelo, the basic idea was that of *set*. In the other, pioneered by Russell and Whitehead, the basic idea was that of *function*. Of course, both of these concepts are fundamental to mathematics and, therefore, in the theory of types, in which function is the basic idea, they had to introduce sets by some sort of trick. The other basic approach—of set theory —had to introduce functions by a trick. It happened to be a rather complicated trick, but was useful, nevertheless. And therefore, if you insist on making sets fundamental, you have to do something very complicated to define functions. It never occurred to mathematical logicians that anyone would ever use this as the basic definition of a function in an elementary course. Somehow, half of this history has been made public; which shows that certain branches of mathematics ought, perhaps, to be classified.

The impression has been created that the *only* way to define a function is in terms of sets. I'll put it to you that research mathematicians never think of a function in this particular manner. They may differ in ways of looking at it—there are three or four different ways—but they have certain similarities, and they are highly intuitive. A function is a mapping, an assignment where you have certain objects in one set, and to each object you assign some specific object, usually from a different set. Now this is a very simple idea, and of a type met in everyday life. Examples familiar to all students can be given.

For example, every human being has a father and a mother. Well, *father* and *mother* are perfectly good functions, defined over the set of human beings, where to each human being "father of" assigns a specific male human being and "mother of" determines a specific female human being. One can illustrate a great many basic ideas connected with functions in terms of simple examples of this sort.

Let me take one of the ideas that has caused most trouble in the study of functions, namely that of the idea of a composite function, where one function is applied to another function. A student may have trouble at first recognizing as a composite function something like $(3x + 2)^4$, but in everyday life it is not terribly hard to explain to him what a maternal grandfather is—father of your mother—and this is a typical composite function.

Actually these simple everyday examples have great pedagogical advantages, because the usual examples of numerical functions are too special for the use of the research mathematician. In advanced mathematics courses you rarely deal with something as simple as a numerical function, and family relations illustrate the general nature of a function much better than do the ordinary numerical functions.

Let us next discuss the simultaneous solution of linear equations (like $3x + 4y = 5$). There is a very elaborate theory in advanced mathematics, known as linear algebra, which has relevance to some of the material being suggested for high school curricula. But if we attempted a complete, rigorous treatment of everything one ought to know about such equations, it would ruin high school algebra, and I don't believe that anyone has ever suggested this.

But what is commonly taught about these equations? It is usually taught as a bag of tricks and techniques which have two serious limitations. One limitation is that these tricks only work in special situations. For example, one of the favorite methods of solving equations—by means of determinants—works only if you happen to have the same number of equations as unknowns and where the key determinant is not zero. So for the advanced mathematician, the solution of an equation by determinants is very rarely of value. (Also, the method as usually taught happens to work only for 3×3 determinants.) The second serious objection is that the methods usually taught for solving simultaneous equations are highly dated and have long lost their practical importance. In the age of computing machines, we must rethink what is a practical way of solving equations and what is an impractical way.

On the related topic of finding roots of an algebraic equation, we had a debate once at Dartmouth about how useful Horner's Method is. I offered to put this to a test. A colleague of mine and I each had a desk computer and a fifth-degree equation for which we had to find a root to five decimal places. He was going to use Horner's Method and I was using successive approximations, i.e., organized common sense. I am sorry to say that this particular test of the practicability of Horner's Method turned out to be quite inconclusive because, unfortunately, I had the root to five decimal places before my colleague remembered Horner's Method. Which was a great pity, because it was the first (and presumably last) time in his career as a professional mathematician that he ever had the least excuse for using Horner's Method.

Let me come back to linear equations. What are some of the key ideas? I think there are two key ideas that one should understand about linear equations, and they do not require tremendous rigor, only a feeling for the subject matter and a degree of understanding. First, one must know what it means to solve simultaneous linear equations, and more generally, what it means to solve equations. A great deal of worthwhile work has been done and various different approaches to this have been suggested. Students should understand that solving an equation will mean finding a certain set of numbers about which a particular assertion is true—about which the equation holds. And solving simultaneous equations means finding a set of numbers about which several assertions hold, in other words, numbers which have all these special properties; in short, finding the intersection of several sets.

Secondly, it is important to connect this idea of a set of solutions with geometry, for one's geometric intuition is usually stronger than one's numerical intuition. For example, if you plot the solution of an equation in two unknowns in the plane, it comes out to be a straight line. If we plot a second equation, it is also represented by a straight line; and to ask for numbers (or rather number pairs) which satisfy both of these equations will obviously be asking for the point or points that the two lines have in common; it is the intersection of the two lines. It is very interesting that when you formulate the same thing set-theoretically, there too the word "intersection" occurs.

Let us illustrate in three dimensions the major theorem that all students should know about simultaneous equations. *One of three things must happen: you may have no solutions; you may have a unique solution; or you may have infinitely many solutions.* This is by far the most important fact known about simultaneous linear equations. There are no solutions, one solution, or infinitely many.

If you think of it geometrically, this fact is obvious. In three dimensions each equation represents a plane. Let us begin with two of them, and let us suppose that they intersect in a line L. Now we ask what happens if we add an additional plane. If we have bad luck, the new plane may be parallel to the line L, and we will have no solution. Normally the new plane will cut L in one and only one point, and we have a unique solution. Or it may happen that the third plane passes through L. In that case we will have infinitely many solutions. This is the most general possible situation for simultaneous linear equations.

It is also easy to see that what happens is not determined by the number of different equations or the number of different unknowns. You could have just two equations in three unknowns and have no solution, because the two planes may be parallel. You may have a hundred different equations in three unknowns and they may still have a unique solution if, by chance, they all go through the same point. And you may have a hundred different equations in three unknowns and you may have infinitely many solutions. Just think of a number of planes, at different angles, all going through a given line.

This simple fact, that I explained here in about five minutes, can be explained to students in one class period. And yet, it is the fundamental fact about solving simultaneous linear equations. It is obvious, *if you teach it intuitively.*

I feel very strongly that, although a degree of rigor is important in teaching because a student should be able to understand what a proof is, it is vastly more important to emphasize basic ideas and to build up the intuition possessed by the student.

Of course, we do not know what constitutes intuition. Even what is intuitively obvious can be a matter of great controversy. You know that the mathematician's favorite word is "trivial," which is a shorthand way of saying "intuitively obvious." There are endless stories about the word "trivial." My favorite is the one about the mathematician who, in a lecture, asserted that a result is trivial. One of his colleagues challenged him, and they got into a long argument which was still going on at the end of the class. The class tiptoed out, and the two mathematicians were seen arguing vehemently for over two hours. When they finally showed up outside, students eagerly queried the challenger about the outcome. He replied: "Oh, he was right. It *is* trivial."

While I maintain that *rigor* is not a necessity in much high school mathematics teaching, I feel quite differently about *abstraction,* which has been tied to it (somewhat accidentally) in many developments. Mathematics by its very nature is abstract. It is the power of abstraction that enables mankind to rise above lower animals. The power to abstract should be developed in students as early as possible.

There has been a feeling that the only way to teach abstraction is to take an abstract axiom system and develop it in detail. This is a worthwhile undertaking; I am not criticizing it. But this is not the only way to develop a feeling for abstraction.

Abstraction should start from simple, concrete examples. An idea can be abstract and still be highly intuitive. For example, a measure space is a very important abstract concept. It is an advanced idea, but it can be explained in the simplest possible terms. (I personally like to do it in terms of probabilities, though it can be done in other ways.)

Just take a collection of objects, say a set of five objects, and assign a weight to each one. Think of each subset as being weighed, literally, by putting all the weights in the subset on scales. This can be used to introduce the basic idea of a measure space. If the weights are all positive and happen to add up to one, you have begun to do probability theory. If the weights don't necessarily add up to one, you may be measuring areas; and if we allow negative weights, then you are doing generalized measure theory—which you are not supposed to be doing until graduate school. It is a natural generalization then to go over to an abstract approach to the idea of area, and a student can see that some of the basic rules governing area govern much wider ranges of mathematical and applied disciplines. Indeed, eventually these same rules are going to apply to all kinds of integrals found in geometry, in physics, in applications, and in several advanced branches of mathematics.

A second important role of abstraction is to connect unrelated ideas. If you have a large number of unrelated ideas, you have to get quite a distance away from them to be able to get a view of all of them, and this is the role of abstraction. If you look at each one too closely, you see too many details. You have to go far away to see what they have in common. And it is by no means true that if you get far away things are going to become less clear. They may appear simpler, because you can only see the large, broad outlines; you do not get lost in petty details. This has been the secret of a great deal of modern mathematics.

Let me take up two unorthodox examples, one from algebra and one from geometry. In algebra, let us select the idea of an *isomorphism,* which is central in modern algebra. Two structures which are alike are said to be isomorphic. More precisely, you've got two sets and you do something with each of them. If you can match up the objects in the two sets in such a way that whenever you do something in one, exactly the same thing happens to corresponding elements in the other set, then one speaks of an isomorphism. This concept is useful because it is so general.

Let us apply it to something that is well known to you; let us apply it to real numbers and to the operations of multiplication and addition. Take two sets: one consists of the positive real numbers, and the other collection has all the real numbers in it. I'm going to concentrate on one type of operation for each of them. In the first set it will be multiplication; in the second set it will be addition. Let us ask whether we can establish an isomorphism. Is it possible to match up the positive real numbers with all the real numbers in such a way that every time you multiply two positive numbers, and you add the corresponding real numbers, the results will correspond? The answer is "yes," even if we require a "continuous" matching.

As a matter of fact, if you try doing this, you quickly convince yourself that you have a certain amount of freedom. If I use the letter f to stand for the correspondence, and I take the positive real number one, we first find that what will correspond to it will be zero (because if you think of your basic laws of multiplication, one plays exactly the same role for multiplication as zero plays for addition), i.e., $f(1) = 0$. If you try raising positive numbers to powers, you will quickly find that this operation corresponds to multiplication, i.e., $f(x^y) = y \cdot f(x)$. After all, raising to powers is essentially repeated multiplication, and hence should correspond to repeated addition, which is multiplication. This formula almost gives us our complete matching, namely, all we have to do is to find a number b, such that $f(b) = 1$. The moment you have found that number, b^y will correspond to $y \cdot f(b)$, which is y, and then you have found the whole secret of how to match the two sets. What you have, of course, are logarithms to the base b.

The amount of choice you have is the freedom of choosing a base for logarithms. You quickly find that your base can be anything except one, and therefore you will have as many different isomorphisms here as you can choose bases for logarithms—any positive real number other than one.

If you look at the same mapping in the opposite direction, you have exponential functions. This is one of many useful ways of looking at logarithms and exponentials; what they really do is establish an isomorphism, a complete structural matching-up, of the positive real numbers under multiplication with real numbers under addition.

I am going to select my other example from topology, the celebrated abstract version of geometry. Let me quote a famous result and show you something that can be done with it. Take any simple polyhedron, and count the number of vertices, the number of faces, and the number of edges. For example, in a box you find eight corners, so the number of vertices is equal to eight. The number of faces on a box is equal to six. And the number of edges—there are four on top, there are four on the bottom, and there are four on the sides—so there are 12 edges. The number of vertices, plus the number of faces, is 14; if you subtract the number of edges, you get two. A remarkable fact, discovered by Euler, is that you can take absolutely any simple polyhedron—any three-dimensional figure with straight edges and plane faces, without holes—and you will always get two as an answer. For example, for a tetrahedron, you get four vertices plus four faces, which equals eight; subtract six edges, and you get two. You can reshape the figure as you like, except that you must not cut a hole in it, because this is a topological property. Actually, there is a more general formula where the number of holes enters into the formula. There are also formulas for other numbers of dimensions.

This fascinating topic should, even without proofs, interest a great many high school students.

But how can we tie this abstract idea to high school topics? Well, for example, one rather isolated, interesting topic in solid geometry (or what is left of solid geometry) is the study of the five regular polyhedra. But why are there just five of them? We will use Euler's formula to answer the question.

Let there be f faces, each being a regular polygon of s sides, and let k faces meet at each vertex. Then the number of edges is $sf/2$ and the number of vertices is sf/k. Hence Euler's formula asserts that $f + sf/k - sf/2 = 2$ or

$$(2k + 2s - ks)f = 4k.$$

Obviously, k and s must be at least three. Thus there are only five possible combinations of integer value for k and s, since larger values would make the left side zero or negative:

$$k = 3, \quad s = 3, \quad f = 4 \qquad \text{(tetrahedron)};$$
$$k = 3, \quad s = 4, \quad f = 6 \qquad \text{(cube)};$$
$$k = 3, \quad s = 5, \quad f = 12 \qquad \text{(dodecahedron)};$$
$$k = 4, \quad s = 3, \quad f = 8 \qquad \text{(octahedron)};$$
$$k = 5, \quad s = 3, \quad f = 20 \qquad \text{(icosahedron)}.$$

This simple mixture of intuition and rigorous proof shows us why there are just five regular solids.

Whatever you may think about my views on rigor, intuition, and abstraction, I hope that we have one common goal, to develop in students early their ability to create new ideas. I feel that able students need only a slight lead, especially if you are fortunate enough to have sections in which you separate off the good students. Once they are amongst their peers they can be encouraged to develop ideas freely; though a certain amount of guidance is very important even here.

I recently finished teaching at a summer institute that Dartmouth co-sponsored. In addition to a number of high school teachers we had two dozen very able secondary school juniors. It was an interesting and enlightening experience. The students were wonderful; I would be happy to have had any one of them at Dartmouth. It was an outstandingly able group, but they were badly in need of some channeling of their unguided mathematical abilities. They seemed to be under the impression that the highest possible use of high school mathematics is solving puzzles. This is not too surprising since high school libraries usually have mathematics sections loaded with puzzle books. The rest of their time was spent on problems of the same sort as they had for homework, only harder— something that took more time or ingenuity. Of course, this has some value, but a really good student should be given a task that is somewhat higher and more challenging to him than doing hard versions of homework problems or solving uninstructive puzzles.

The first thing that we can all do is to give the students a good book to read. An able high school student is old enough to read books. There are many books on the market that can be given to a student. SMSG (School Mathematics Study Group, Stanford University) is undertaking a major effort to turn out special pamphlets and monographs for just this type of use in high school, and other groups are doing the same. A list compiled by Mu Alpha Theta (Box 1155, University of Oklahoma, Norman, Oklahoma) tried to prove to you that for $180 you can build up a superb high school mathematics collection. And, indeed, that list with $180 worth of books in it is more than enough for any high school collection. Half of it would do very well. I was pleasantly surprised by the number and quality of really good books that are available and readable by high school students.

Even better than giving them books is to give them *good* problems. There are lots of good problems suitable for students. Take a book like that marvelous one by Professor G. Pólya, *Induction and Analogy in Mathematics* (Princeton, N.J.: Princeton University Press, 1954). I will cite just one of his classic examples. He asks the question, "Suppose you have a number of planes, say 10 planes, and you partition a room with these; into how many pieces will a room be cut with ten partitions? How about n partitions?" I assure you that it is not an easy problem, unless you go at it just right. The right way to solve the three-dimensional problem is to consider it first in one and two dimensions. In one dimension we have a line with n points on it, and the number of pieces is clearly $n + 1$. Then do it in two dimensions, using the solution of the one-dimensional case, and then go to three dimensions. Your best student will not only have no trouble in doing this, but will come back with the solution for four, five, and—hopefully—for n dimensions.

Or give these students a little bit of number theory—the theory of whole numbers. There are dozens of opportunities for the student to develop his own formulas. Nothing is more thrilling than to find a mathematical formula that holds without exception. If you want them to do geometry, why stick to three-dimensional geometry? It is rather dull. Why not let them do four- or five-dimensional geometry? Let them try to argue by analogy (or rigorously, if they can) theorems in four- and five-dimensional geometry, using their experience in two and three dimensions. If you want to do abstract algebra, the beginnings of the theory of groups are easily accessible to a high school group. I have often used that as a talk for high school students. The vast majority of them grasped the idea the first time. I certainly don't say that you should do this in a single lecture, but spend a week on it, then challenge them to go out and develop their own examples of groups. Finally—if they are really ambitious—let them form their own axiom system for something more abstract, let them work it out, and see for themselves what actually happens.

I think in all fields we owe it to our best students to encourage creative endeavor. The great advantage that we have in mathematics is that, again and again, examples have shown it possible to get students at a remarkably early age to do creative mathematics. There have been major contributions to mathematics by men in their late teens. Even if your students aren't going to do creative work, at least give them a first taste of developing something that may not be new to the mathematical world, but is new to them; something that has not been spoon-fed, but that they have honestly discovered for themselves—preferably something that you, yourself, have never heard of. I know that at first it is frightening to have your students know something you don't know, but it is the greatest achievement of a teacher to enable his students to surpass him.

I would like to close by citing the example of Galois, the great young French mathematician. He died at the age of 21, yet he will remain for all time one of the great creative mathematicians because in his late teens he created entirely new ideas, the first really deep insight into group theory. This will remain fundamental mathematics for centuries to come. Galois's biography is more fascinating than any currently featured on television, but it is also very disturbing. He had to fight against traditional school curricula that strait-jacketed thinking, and against teachers who neither understood nor had tolerance for the unorthodox mind. His good fortune was to be exposed to writings of Legendre, Lagrange, and Abel, and to find one high school teacher with the vision to encourage the young genius. What would be the fate of Galois today? Would he find anyone to encourage him in exploring entirely new paths, and would anyone help him find the mathematical literature that would inspire him, or would he be doomed to eternal boredom by being kept within the limitations of the traditional curriculum?

6 THE MATHEMATICALLY TALENTED STUDENT

From Grade School to Graduate School *

THE PROBLEM

It is a common misconception to associate mathematical talent with rare genius. If mathematical talent were indeed restricted to the one in a million, I would not be here speaking to you today, nor would you trouble to come and listen to me.

Just how widespread is mathematical talent? I have often quizzed grade school teachers on the subject, and the typical answer was somewhat as follows: "There are usually one or two outstanding students in each grade school class, and two or three more who show a strong interest in arithmetic." If one tries to extrapolate from this to the whole population of the United States, this would indicate 10 million people in the United States with definite mathematical talent, and perhaps as many as 25 million who have at an early age shown a definite liking and ability for arithmetic. What happens to these students in later life?

First let us look at various occupations that require a significant amount of mathematical talent. Government, industry, and our universities employ approximately 90,000 mathematicians and physical scientists. If one adds to this high school mathematics teachers, the number is increased significantly. A much larger group is the number of engineers; while this number runs as high as a million, it probably includes a great many specialties requiring little or no mathematical talent. But it is fair to say that, including a number of other occupations not here listed, there must be at least half a million people in the United States who depend on mathematical talent and serious mathematical training for their livelihood. The

* Reprinted with permission from the *Bulletin of the National Association of Secondary School Principals,* April 1963. Copyright: Washington, D. C.

number may be higher than that—probably more than one per cent of the total labor force.

The problem of the mathematically talented student would be worth considering, even if he represented only one out of every 100 people working in the United States. However, the problem is much greater than this.

First of all, many of the professions I have mentioned so far are tremendously understaffed and demands on them are increasing rapidly. The President's Scientific Advisory Committee has recommended that the number of doctoral degrees in mathematics and the sciences be more than doubled in the next decade. This will be an extremely difficult task.

Speaking to a group of secondary school principals, I don't have to dwell on the shortage of high school mathematics teachers. If your school has not had difficulty in recent years filling a vacancy, then you are exceptional indeed. Universities are flooded with begging requests from government and industry to help fill vast numbers of well-paying vacancies, principal demands being mathematical talent and advanced mathematical training.

The computing industry alone could absorb all men and women receiving mathematical degrees for the next ten years. And the number of fields that now require mathematical talent are increasing rapidly. For example, the biological-social sciences now demand a significant amount of college-level mathematics, and even business schools are beginning to use sophisticated modern mathematical methods.

In short, we find that perhaps 25 million adults in the United States have at grade school age shown a definite interest in arithmetic, but only two per cent of these pursue this to the point where they actually earn a living based on this talent. If the new age of science is to flourish in the United States, if research is to keep up with ever-increasing demands, and if the level of teaching mathematics and related fields in the colleges and secondary schools is not to be lowered, then a much larger percentage of mathematically talented students must be encouraged to pursue this talent. This is the problem I would like to discuss with you: *How can we capture the imagination of the large number of mathematically talented grade school students, keep up their interest through high school, and guide them through our colleges and graduate schools, to one of the dozens of careers that pay rich dividends for this specialized talent?*

CURRICULUM REFORM

In speaking to parents, one gathers the impression that students are frightened by the difficulty of mathematics and therefore stop studying it as early as permissible. However, I have overwhelming evidence that with mathematically talented students exactly the opposite is the case. Many more able students are bored out of mathematics than frightened out of it. I would list as the three principal causes of losing talented mathematics students boredom, poor instruction, and an outdated curriculum.

The problem of the outdated curriculum is now being attacked on a national scale. The attempts to reform mathematics teaching started on the college level a decade ago, and have now gained great momentum in secondary schools and are beginning to spread to primary education.

It is fair to say that in the year 1950, mathematics instruction in the United States was about 150 years behind mathematical research. While it certainly takes time for new developments to filter from research journals to our colleges, and eventually to secondary and primary education, a 150 year lag in a rapidly changing field is inexcusable. It is hard to imagine anyone teaching a high school physics course, even for a single year, without mentioning many of the discoveries of the twentieth century. At the same time, our high school mathematics program did not even mention the great discoveries of the nineteenth century.

Although we are still very far from seeing a modern curriculum all over the country, the trend is entirely in the right direction. Our colleges are increasingly teaching modern mathematics side by side with the important parts of classical mathematics. Our secondary schools have benefited greatly from a large number of excellent experimental projects, financed both by the government and privately, which have allowed the development of highly improved curricula. The major change on the high school level has been that traditional topics are taught now from a modern point of view, and modern subjects are woven into the curriculum wherever appropriate.

The large number of topics that were in the curriculum only because they had been there for such a long time that nobody would think of omitting them, have now been reexamined, and, although the many worthwhile topics have been retained, the waste has been eliminated. It is only in the last three or four years that serious efforts have been made to carry out a similar program on the primary level. We can look forward to vast progress in this area within the next decade.

This leaves the twin problems of poor instruction and boredom for the outstanding student. Let us examine these problems level by level and consider what steps could be taken to improve the situation.

THE GRADE SCHOOL

Most students have their basic attitude towards mathematics shaped in grade school.

The grade school teacher in the United States is supposed to be an omniscient being fully expert in all major areas of learning, capable of inspiring the student with love for languages, literature, arithmetic, science, social science, love of the community, and whatever else the local grade school curriculum requires. One must face the fact that such all-around geniuses do not exist.

Although very hard-working and devoted grade school teachers do the best they can, it is bound to happen that they will be stronger in some areas and weaker in others. They, themselves, are the product of past sins in mathematical education; therefore, more often than not, their weakest subject is arithmetic. It is also true that the mathematical education of grade school teachers has been scandalously neglected, so that in many parts of the country it is possible for a teacher to teach arithmetic through sixth grade or even eighth grade without having elected a high school mathematics course. The Mathematical Association of America has recommended minimum standards for grade school teachers, consisting of two years of substantial high school mathematics, followed by two years of college mathematics specially designed for grade school teachers. Only a small minority of grade school teachers could meet these qualifications at the present time.

A study of the Carnegie Corporation, a number of years ago, brought out an even more dangerous factor: most new grade school teachers now being produced not only fail to be mathematically talented, but actually have an active dislike for mathematics. If there is one lesson that modern psychology has taught us, it is the fact that students at primary school age are tremendously impressionable, and that both the parents and the grade school teacher make lasting impressions on them. A single year spent in a classroom taught by a teacher with an active dislike for arithmetic could mar a child's own attitude toward mathematics for life.

There are a number of steps that could be taken to improve this situation: first of all, grade school teachers should be required to have a more substantial mathematical background. This would give them more confidence in the classroom, and therefore they are less likely to be antagonistic toward the subject. Secondly, the evidence is overwhelming that some of the new curricula are more fun to teach and more fun to learn than the old-fashioned arithmetic programs. I have had most heartening testimony from teachers in our own grade school in Hanover, N.H. Since we have changed to a modern arithmetic program, even teachers who previously disliked arithmetic are having fun with it. But if these steps are not sufficient to solve the problem, the day may not be far away when we have to use arithmetic specialists on a wide scale, at least in the upper primary grades.

If the picture is somewhat dismal for the *average* student as far as arithmetic learning is concerned, think of how bad the situation is for the few *mathematically talented* students in each class. The grade school teacher has her hands full, teaching arithmetic to a fairly large class, and she is sure to have three or four students who are having tremendous difficulties absorbing elementary arithmetic. Therefore, if she has any time to spare, she is likely to spend it on the below-average students. When the good student finishes his work in record time, the teacher will be slightly annoyed, and will do one of two things: Either she will give him 10 more of the same problems to do, which is sure to bore him to tears, or she will tell him, "Well, now that you have gotten arithmetic out of the way, you can have some fun. Go do some extra reading." It is a rare arithmetic teacher, indeed, who has the mathematical preparation and the interest to give substantial enrichment materials to the few exceptional students in the class.

About the only solution so far suggested has been the acceleration of the really bright student. But this is hardly practical on the grade school level. The usual result is that the student in second grade finishes half the work that he would normally take in third grade, and then has to repeat the same work in third grade. This is most discouraging. Instead of that, each grade school classroom should be provided with ample materials to enrich the required curriculum, problems that go deeper and require more original thought than the routine problems, and ones that students could be left to do on their own.

The grade school teacher should also be instructed to take the few extra moments in the day necessary to give encouragement and advice to the bright student. If a school has arithmetic specialists, they could pay special attention to the able student. But even a school without specialists will usually find that one or two grade school teachers have a definite liking for the subject, and perhaps they could take mathematically talented students from several different classes twice a week to give them extra encouragement.

THE SECONDARY SCHOOL

Let me now turn to the problems on the secondary school level, which, after all, interest you gentlemen most of all. There is one observation that underlies all my following remarks. There is no other field of knowledge where there is as great a difference between the most talented and least talented student as in mathematics. There is something in the very nature of the subject matter that brings out extreme ability or lack of ability in the human mind. For this reason I feel it essential to separate the best and the weakest students in your secondary school classes. Indeed, if at all possible, I should like to see this done at least as early as fourth grade.

I realize that ability grouping is often a controversial topic, but whether your own institution does this in any other field or not, I feel that it is a must in mathematics. If your school graduates as many as 100 students a year, you should be able to afford special sections for the mathematically talented and interested students. If your School Board, or Board of Education, questions the additional expense involved in such a section, let me, as a member of the Hanover, N. H., School Board, answer the question for you:

> Civilization has a tremendous stake in the development of mathematical talent. Our highly complex scientific civilization cannot function unless we have a sufficient number of mathematicians, physicists, engineers, and scientists of all types who have had adequate mathematical training. You, the citizens of this and other communities, are making tremendous demands on mathematical talents in the running of your businesses, the millions of gadgets in your homes, your television sets, your transportation systems, and in dozens of other ways. Developing mathematical and scientific talent may be more expensive than other demands you make, but if you demand this, you must be willing to pay for it.

Next there is the question of whether it is fair to separate out a relatively small number of really able students. This I want to answer categorically, by saying that both the students separated out and the students not separated out would profit. If you teach mathematics in mixed sections, the teacher has to teach on two or three entirely different levels. The mathematically talented students will be three steps ahead of everyone else, and will continually pester the teacher with reasonable questions, but questions which mean nothing to the majority of the class. Should the teacher teach to the average student and let the mathematical talent go to waste or should he spend a substantial amount of time encouraging this talent and therefore deny the majority of the class the instruction that they deserve?

I would also like to say, from many years' experience, that there is nothing else you can do to make your mathematics staff as happy as to have these special honors sections for your best mathematics teachers to teach. In one's entire career as a teacher, be it on the high school level, college level, or graduate school level, there is no experience more satisfying than half a year or a year spent encouraging the best mathematical talent.

MATHEMATICS FOR THE TALENTED HIGH SCHOOL STUDENT

I am almost prepared to say that, once you have your best students separated out, the problem is solved. Because, if the teacher does not do a good job teaching the class, it is very likely that the class will do an excellent job teaching itself. However, this is not quite true. The major thing lacking, even in the brightest group of mathematically talented students, is an understanding of what mathematics is about and judgement as to what constitutes good and fruitful mathematics, and what are simply amusing puzzles.

How should the curriculum of a mathematically able class differ from that of other classes? It is very likely that these students will rush through the required material in half the allowed time, and acquire a much better understanding of it than the majority of other students. To some extent the answer can be acceleration, but I would personally hope that this is not the complete answer. Certainly, the traditional curriculum proceeded much too slowly. There is no good reason why ninth-grade algebra should not find its way to eighth grade, or even to seventh grade, with exceptional students. However, rushing through mathematics is not a goal in itself.

What is much more important is a deeper and more thorough-going understanding of the nature of mathematics and of its various branches. The real education of the mathematically talented student begins where the others have left off. While most students will learn mathematics as a collection of separate topics, which may or may not be amusing or useful in themselves, the mathematically talented student should acquire an over-all view of the structure of mathematics. If this is to be at all successful, it must start in grade school and proceed right on to graduate school. If there is any one major crime in the traditional curriculum, it is the fact that the basic unified structure of mathematics is not brought out and that the tremendously important interrelations between branches of mathematics are ignored.

To some extent this may be simply an attempt to simplify the problems. It is much easier to teach algebra on the one hand and geometry on the other hand, rather than to show that geometry problems can be solved by means of algebra, or that algebraic problems are illuminated by looking at them geometrically. But the secret of mathematical success is precisely the ability to apply tools from one branch of mathematics to another branch of mathematics. For example, the marriage of algebra and geometry showed up in classical mathematics as analytic geometry, while in modern mathematics it shows up as the powerful branches of linear algebra and algebraic geometry, both with far-reaching theoretical consequences and the former also yielding tremendously important practical applications.

Fortunately, within the last few years many different agencies have developed new materials that serve as enrichment work for grade school and high school students. If a teacher of an advanced section can do nothing else, at least he should have at hand many of these materials and bring them to the attention of the students. The talented mathematics student is likely to go out on his own and search for more mathematics to learn, and here he could be badly misled. I was greatly shocked, in looking at the mathematics collection of one of the best secondary schools in the country, to find that more than half the books of the collection were books of mathematical puzzles. This is one of many temptations that one must resist in teaching able students. Mathematical puzzles are like peanuts: once you get started, it is very difficult to stop eating them, but they do not constitute a healthy diet in themselves. Puzzles are amusing, sometimes they are very difficult, and hence are challenging to the bright student. Students will compete in solving them, and it's such an easy thing to give for the entertainment of bright students. But puzzles are not mathematics.

A similar temptation is to enrich a class by adding hard problems. Again, the solution of hard problems is one facet of mathematical training, but it is only one facet, and not all of mathematics. Each year one finds a number of highly talented mathematics students who come to college with the impression that all of mathematics consists of the solving of hard problems. These students usually have a blind spot, and find it very difficult to progress to new branches of mathematics. Mathematics is first, and above everything else, a systematic, abstract study, and problems serve merely as illustrations or as a by-product of mathematical work. Mathematical theory must reign supreme.

Above all, the major goal of mathematical education in high school is to teach the student to reason for himself. With the mathematically talented student, this often takes a minimum of encouragement. It may be quite enough if the teacher does not *penalize* the student for thinking for himself. Unlike the traditional belief that mathematics consists in memorizing a great many highly dull facts, mathematics is the one field where the human mind has great freedom in developing its ingenuity for logical reasoning.

I vividly remember a high school teacher who penalized me in a geometry class because the proof I gave for a theorem was different from the proof in the book. Indeed, when I tried to ask her what was wrong with my own proof, she did not understand my question: clearly, the book has a proof of the theorem, therefore it was THE correct proof of the theorem. Instead, the teacher of the mathematically talented student should expect the student to do it better than the teacher half of the time, and one out of ten times better than the book does it.

A final word of warning on what I call "gimmicks." I am particularly concerned over the fact that science fairs, which are otherwise highly worthwhile institutions, have a tendency of encouraging mathematical gimmicks. At such fairs the judges look at the various exhibits and in order that someone should have a reasonable chance of winning, the exhibit must have considerable visual appeal. This has the tendency of discouraging theoretical work in the sciences and of discouraging most of the important mathematical projects. I get dozens of letters each year from students who wish help in a science fair, and I am discouraged that the vast majority of them simply look for projects that will have a spectacular-looking object in it, whether it has any mathematical significance or not. Perhaps a science fair is not the right place to encourage mathematics.

However, it is important to encourage the pursuit of mathematics outside the classroom. A mathematics club is a natural place for such encouragement. Hopefully, a mathematics club would not be organized around gimmicks, but around serious mathematical topics not normally taken up in the classroom. Fortunately, mathematics abounds in such topics. Students should be encouraged to do substantial outside reading and to present this to the club. Also, a nearby university or the Mathematical Association of America may be able to provide a visiting mathematician who can speak of current mathematical activities from first-hand experience.

Equally important is the possibility of mathematical competitions. Students are generally encouraged by rivalry, and such contests as the one sponsored for all high schools in the United States by the Mathematical Association of America are carefully designed to encourage the right kind of interest in mathematics.

The advent of computing machines provides an additional opportunity for encouraging mathematical talent. Programming for a high-speed computer requires the type of systematic thought, ingenuity, and logical precision that is excellent training for the mathematically talented student. This is particularly true in his late high school and beginning college years. Since there is a critical shortage of mathematical programmers in the country, a shortage that is likely to get much worse before it improves, more and more computing centers are providing time for students to encourage an interest in this activity. If high schools are fortunate enough to be located near such a computing center, they should take full advantage of it. The day is also rapidly approaching when there will be good inexpensive high-speed computing machines available for high schools, or where large computing centers could be shared by a number of institutions.

I should like to add a word about the guidance high school students receive. From having talked to a number of college freshmen, I am under the impression that a great many guidance departments are out of date on the question of how much mathematics a student should take. Certainly, as far as admission to college is concerned, it is still true that one or two years of high school mathematics will get you into many colleges; three years, or even two and a half years are usually enough for the best colleges, unless you are going to go into mathematics, physics, or engineering, and only a small minority of students are required to show four years of mathematics at entrance. However, this is far from a complete story. It is one thing to get into college; it is quite a different proposition to prepare for a career in college.

Most of the better colleges are rapidly cutting down on pre-calculus courses. Therefore, the student who does not enter college prepared for a course in the calculus may have cut himself off from a much larger number of possible careers than his guidance counselor would have led him to believe. Equally important is the fact that many scientific careers—for example, medicine—require such a tremendous number of college courses that a student who has not taken full advantage of high school mathematics has little chance to make up for this deficiency in college. It is common to find an eminent doctor who finds, years later, that his mathematical preparation was insufficient for a research project he has to undertake. Even more common nowadays is the social scientist who pays dearly in graduate school for the omissions in high school and early college years. After several years' interruption, it is very difficult to get back into the swing of mathematical education. And often it is only during his graduate education that the social scientist finds out that he cannot read the current literature and cannot understand the latest thinking in his own field without substantially more mathematical training than he has acquired. It is particularly sad to hear "I always liked mathematics, but since I went into such-and-such field, I thought there was no point in continuing it."

This brings me to the greatest waste of mathematical talent in the United States. I firmly believe that there are just as many girls who are mathematically talented as boys. However, there are a number of social factors, which combine with the advice that they receive, to lead girls to discontinue mathematics. Very early, girls find out that excellence in languages is an acceptable trait in a girl, but outdoing a boy in mathematics will not be tolerated. I am sure that my wife's experience in being talked out of taking trigonometry, because she was going to be the only girl in the class, is not uncommon.

It is a crime to see a tremendous amount of mathematical talent going to waste, when so many of the positions now vacant for lack of men could be filled just as capably by women, who were needlessly discouraged. I would think that encouraging mathematical talent would be particularly good for a woman who plans to raise a family, since there are many jobs that she could hold down, later in life, on a part-time basis. I wish that each guidance counselor who is told by a girl that she does not wish to continue mathematics would take five minutes to find out whether the girl has really lost interest in the subject or is discontinuing it for irrelevant social considerations.

COLLEGE MATHEMATICS

This brings me to the problems on the college level. Of course, this problem is closest to my own heart, since I have devoted my own life to an attempt to make some improvement in collegiate mathematical education.

Here we are faced by a tremendous diversity in the interests of the students and in their mathematical needs. In Dartmouth College we have tried to design a curriculum which will meet all of these needs. In addition to the straightforward mathematics program, which prepares the student for any one of dozens of mathematical occupations, we have special sequences for physical science students on the one hand and biological and social science students on the other hand. And, in addition to these three basic sequences, there is the honors program, of which we are particularly proud.

Over 90 per cent of Dartmouth freshmen elect mathematics, even though there is no mathematics required at the college. Of these, about 10 per cent are selected for special sections of the mathematically talented. The first two years of the honors program are designed for all mathematically talented and interested students, whatever their future careers may be. In these sections we try to encourage those students who have already developed a genuine love for mathematics, and try to kindle new flames for students who have never before seen mathematics in its purest and most fascinating form.

The basic philosophy of these sections is similar to what I have outlined for the secondary level. The required material is covered in a relatively short time, and then the students are exposed to materials designed to give them a deeper understanding and to challenge their originality of thinking. We also encourage students to ask questions outside the material to be discussed. It's not uncommon to spend an entire hour talking of "irrelevant" mathematics. Indeed, I have characterized the difference between the honors sections and the regular sections by saying that when a class is told that a given topic is not required for the final examination, the regular sections go to sleep, and the honors sections wake up.

It is in these honors sections that we see the degree to which mathematical talent is wasted on earlier levels. It is very common to find a student who goes into an honors section reluctantly, because he claims to have no particular interest in mathematics, only to find out later that there is nothing he wants to do more than to become a mathematician. We now have several outstanding graduate students at leading universities who entered Dartmouth with no intention of studying mathematics.

The best of these students who finish the two-year program and decide to major in mathematics constitute the heart of our honors program. These students are given complete freedom and proceed at a rapid pace, so that they soon study graduate-level mathematics. It is exciting to watch the development of that rare degree of mathematical talent found only in a small number of students, when it is coupled with a genuine drive to learn mathematics. We were greatly pleased that, during last year's national mathematics competitions (the Putnam Exam), where over 200 colleges competed, out of the 30 students receiving at least honorable mention, four were from Dartmouth College. In this we were second only to Harvard University and far ahead of other institutions of the size of Dartmouth.

Many of these students are also employed as research assistants, in which capacity they assist faculty members in their research projects. The very best of them are encouraged, during their junior and senior years, to work on problems of their own, and about once a year we find an undergraduate who makes a significant mathematical discovery. But, above all, our aim at this level is to give them the best possible preparation for graduate work in mathematics. Since the United States turns out only 300 Ph.D.'s a year in mathematics, we feel that if we can send five to 10 outstanding graduate students in mathematics to the leading graduate schools each year, Dartmouth College will be making more than its share of contributions to future mathematical education and research.

Nor do we neglect the various fields that make use of mathematics. Students who come through our basic honors program turn out to be outstanding graduate students in physics, engineering, biology, and the social sciences. A special "applied honors major" in the department is likely to become a significant training program for the future theoreticians in psychology, sociology, and economics.

Colleges share many problems with high schools. The curriculum must be updated. There is a shortage of well-qualified and interested college teachers. And college mathematics departments have only recently faced up to the necessity of instituting honors programs for the mathematically talented. If there is any special crime of which our colleges can be accused, it is the fact that mathematics departments have neglected the needs of students other than future mathematicians and physical scientists. We have tended to close our eyes to the much larger number of biological, social science, and business students who are beginning to require a substantial amount of college mathematics. When more colleges and universities develop special mathematics programs for the needs of these students, we will see much less wasted mathematical talent.

THE GRADUATE SCHOOL

This brings me to the graduate school level. You may feel that this is a topic remote from your own interests, but I would like to convince you otherwise.

If we are to relieve the critical shortage of high school mathematics teachers, our colleges must train well qualified men and women for these positions. Our colleges cannot accomplish this without a significant increase in the number of college mathematics teachers in the country. And thus we must face the problem of graduate education in mathematics.

On this level, the problem is the opposite of that faced earlier: the exceptionally talented student receives tremendous encouragement, but the much larger number of mathematically able and interested students, who may not meet the qualifications of "the genius," are neglected. I am afraid that most of our graduate schools are interested only in training the research mathematician, who may or may not do some teaching in his spare time. The major development that will be necessary in graduate education in the United States is a broadening of the mathematics graduate programs to take into account the needs of college mathematics teachers, who may or may not do research in addition to their teaching.

A significant step forward was a conference at Yale University in October of 1961, attended by representatives of some 35 graduate mathematics departments. At this conference it was recommended that the requirements for the traditional Ph.D. in mathematics be broadened, so that graduate schools may award Ph.D.'s for a wider variety of mathematical talent. For example, at many institutions in the future, a man will be able to earn a Ph.D. in mathematics for any outstanding piece of scholarship, even if it does not involve the creation of new mathematics. If this is followed up by a similar change in the attitude of graduate school professors, it will, in the long run, be a most significant improvement, and it will affect the entire scale of mathematical education in the United States.

We at Dartmouth College are proud to be one of the first institutions to attempt to implement this broader Ph.D. program. I would love to report far-reaching favorable developments on this level at Dartmouth, but since the program was launched only last September, I am afraid that you will have to wait another five years for my report.

CONCLUSION

I have tried to argue that there is a vast amount of latent mathematical talent in the United States, but somewhere in the educational process the talent is discouraged, bored, or otherwise lost. It is only by a conscious effort from grade school to graduate school to foster a wide range of mathematical talent, that we can hope to see a significant relief in the shortage of mathematically trained men and women.

I have tried to argue that the most significant steps to be taken are a modernized curriculum, a serious attempt to show the systematic nature of mathematical knowledge, good enrichment materials, and ability grouping. Above all, of course, we must have able mathematics teachers for our talented mathematical students.

I should like to leave you with a special message for the mathematics teachers at your own institutions. If they have an opportunity to teach special sections for mathematically talented students, they will soon discover that there are students in the class who are more able than the teachers. It does not matter at which level you teach, in grade school or graduate school, this is an experience we all share. Some teachers may find this discouraging. But it does not take great talent in teachers to pass on to their students exactly what they themselves know. The most satisfying experience in life is to produce a student who far exceeds our own limitations.

7 MATHEMATICS WITHOUT NUMBERS *

A hundred years ago a mathematician would have defined mathematics as "the study of number and space." Indeed, the Thorndike-Barnhart *Dictionary* published in 1956 still defines mathematics as the "science dealing with numbers and the measurement, properties, and relationships of quantities." The study of numbers led to the development of algebra, and the study of space to geometry. These two disciplines merged in the calculus, the crowning glory of classical mathematics. A significant feature of modern mathematics is that such a definition is much too narrow to include its newer branches.

Classical mathematics was ideally suited for the development of physics. Indeed, it arose from physics in many cases. For innumerable problems in physics on which measurements are readily available, the physicist may use a numerical model. On other problems the physicist is concerned with the nature of physical space, and thus classical geometry is suitable as a model. Even when Euclidean geometry proved to be no longer adequate for the needs of modern physics, Einstein was able to use a mathematical model which combined a non-Euclidean geometry with methods of the calculus. This type of model still fits the description of mathematics as the study of number and space.

The social sciences may be characterized by the fact that in most of their problems numerical measurements seem to be absent and considerations of space are irrelevant. I would like to consider in this paper ways in which mathematical models may be used in connection with typical problems in the social sciences.

Let us consider why a scientist employs mathematical models. First of all, the language of mathematics is a convenient form in which to formulate scientific theories. It forces the theoretician in various sciences to formulate his hypotheses in a precise and unambiguous form. It also forces him to strip the scientific problem of all accidental details. Once the model is formulated in its abstract form, it becomes a branch of mathematics. If the scientist is fortunate, this branch of mathematics will have been studied by mathematicians

* First appeared in the Fall 1959 issue of *Daedelus, Journal of the American Academy of Arts and Sciences*. Reprinted by permission of *Daedelus*.

previously, and then theorems proven in this field become available as predictions for the scientist. For the axioms of the mathematical system, when interpreted, represent scientific theories, and hence the theorems, when interpreted in the same way, are logical consequences of the scientist's theories. In this way the mathematician will have accomplished the logical analysis of scientific theories for the scientist.

It has often been pointed out that the mathematical theorem adds nothing to the hypotheses from which it is deduced. Indeed, if a theorem added to the content of the hypotheses, it would not follow logically from them, and hence it would not be a theorem of the branch of mathematics. However, theorems, though not new in content, may be psychologically new to the scientist, and very often are. In effect, the mathematician says to the scientist, "Did you know that your assumptions imply such and such?" And very often this will come as a pleasant (or unpleasant) surprise to the scientist. The mathematician has bridged the gap between original assumptions and verifiable predictions. He has enabled the scientist to test his hypotheses, and often enables him to make pragmatically significant predictions about the future.

But it sometimes happens that the mathematical model formulated by the scientist does not correspond to any known branch of mathematics. In this case the scientist either must create a new branch of mathematics or must appeal to the mathematician to undertake this task for him. For example, when Newton formulated his Laws of Motion, he found that there was no branch of mathematics suitable for the treatment of his new model. He had to turn to the method of the calculus that he invented. The social scientist today often finds the mathematician unable to enlighten him on the particular model of interest to him. Many mathematicians have the impression that mathematical problems in the social sciences are entirely trivial. On the contrary, most problems in the social sciences are too difficult for present-day mathematics. It is because the problems arising in the social sciences rapidly become difficult that only some of the very simplest mathematical problems have been solved so far.

There is every reason to expect that the various social sciences will serve as incentives for the development of great new branches of mathematics and that some day the theoretical social scientist will have to know more mathematics than the physicist needs to know today.

There are essentially two different ways in which a mathematical model may be formed for a problem that does not involve numbers or space. The first method is to use a branch of mathematics which itself does not employ numbers and does not deal with space. The second method is to introduce numbers by a more or less arbitrary method, where no numbers were at first apparent. Then it may be possible to form a significant numerical model of a nonnumerical problem. Two examples of each of these approaches will be discussed in detail.

The examples to be discussed will employ methods either from modern algebra or from modern geometry. To give a maximum variety to these examples, one algebraic and one geometric model will be discussed for each of the two possible approaches to nonnumerical problems.

MODEL NO. 1

Our first model will employ graph theory, which is a branch of modern geometry, but it may be said to be in no way relevant to the study of space. Thus we will discuss a geometric example of a model in which the problem, to start with, is nonnumerical and nonspatial, and the model formed remains so. The problem to be considered is that of structural balance in a social group.*

We consider a social group with certain information concerning likes and dislikes between pairs of individuals. A graph is a convenient mathematical language in which to represent such a structure.

A *graph* is defined as a set of points with lines connecting some, though not necessarily all, pairs of points. We may allow some of these lines to have arrows on them indicating directions, in which case we speak of a *directed graph*. We may also allow plus and minus signs on some of these lines, in which case we speak of a *signed graph*. If persons A and B are represented by two points, then an arrow from A to B with a plus sign might indicate that A likes B, and one with a minus sign might indicate that A dislikes B. If there is no arrow from A to B, then A is indifferent to B (see Fig. 1).

Figure 1

* The graph model is from D. Cartwright and F. Harary, "Structural Balance: A Generalization of Heider's Theory," *Psychological Review* (1956), **5:** 277–293.

In the problem to be considered we will be interested in conditions under which a social group is in "balance." If A likes B but B does not like A, then there is a lack of balance. The first necessary condition for balance will be that B should always hold the same relation to A that A holds to B. Therefore we need not employ directed graphs; ordinary signed graphs will serve our purpose. These graphs, which have no arrows on the line segments, are suitable for symmetric relations.

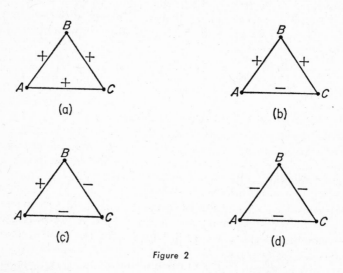

Figure 2

Figure 2 represents the possible signed graphs for three people if no person is indifferent to any other person. In (a), where everyone likes everyone else, the social group is balanced. In (b), where person B likes both the others, but these two dislike each other, there is an unbalanced situation. In (c), A and B like each other and each of them dislikes the third person. This is again a balanced situation. Graph (d) represents a situation in which everyone dislikes everyone else. This may be considered to be unbalanced, as there will be strong forces for pairs of individuals to form a coalition against the third one. It may be observed that the graphs with an even number of minus signs are balanced and the graphs with an odd number of minus signs are unbalanced.

Cartwright and Harary searched the literature for examples in which social scientists had labeled social groups "balanced" or "unbalanced." They noted that all these situations satisfied the following definition: if we take a *cycle* within a graph to be a path starting at A and ending at A, we then define a signed graph to be *balanced* if every cycle in it has an even number of minus signs.

Since this definition subsumed every example they found in the literature, and since it provided a complete definition of balanced social structures, they proposed it as a general definition of structural balance in a social group. Of course it remains for the social scientists to decide whether this is a general, satisfactory definition. Let us assume for the moment that it is.

We now have a mathematical model for structural balance in a social group. Since we have the tools of graph theory available to us, let us search for a theorem of graph theory that would lead to an interesting conclusion concerning social groups. Such an example is the *structure theorem* for signed graphs. This theorem may be stated as follows: a signed graph is balanced if, and only if, it is possible to subdivide the points into two sets, such that all positive connections occur between points in the same set and all negative connections occur between points in different sets.

This theorem has a most interesting interpretation in terms of political science. Let us suppose that we have a political body with likes, dislikes, and indifferences between pairs of members. Or, if we prefer, we may replace likes by "ability to get along politically." Let us say that "it is possible to impose a two-party structure" on the political body if there is a method of dividing the members of the political body into two parties, so that any one member likes members only of his own party and dislikes members only of the other party. This holds under the alternate interpretation if any one member can get along only with members of his own party and fails to get along politically only with members of the opposing party. Then the structure theorem says simply that a political body is balanced if, and only if, it is possible to impose a two-party structure on it.

This result, which may be surprising to the social scientist, is a good example of the pure mathematician contributing a useful theorem.

MODEL NO. 2

The second model employs group theory, a branch of modern algebra in which numbers need play no role at all. Specifically, we will be concerned with a group of transformations.

A *group of transformations* may be characterized as follows: we are given a set of objects S and a certain collection G of "changes" on S. That is, each element of G may be used to change an object of S into some other (or possibly the same) object of S. For these transformations G to form a *group*, two conditions must be satisfied. First the changes must come in pairs: for every transformation g_1 there must be a transformation g_2, so that g_2 always undoes what g_1 did, and vice versa; that is, if g_1 changes an object s into an object t, then g_2 must change the object t into the object s. The second condition is that the result of performing two transformations, one after the other, should again be a transformation within G. Thus if g_1 takes s into t, and g_2 takes t into u, then g_3 will change s directly into u. This may be thought of simply as a mental attitude on our part, in that we always decide to include the "combined transformation" g_3 in our collection G.

The reader will note the extremely general nature of the concept of a group of transformations. Yet there is a vast literature on groups of transformations, and hence a tremendous number of theorems that may be employed any time such a group is available to us.

Marriage rules in primitive societies have been studied from a mathematical point of view by André Weil and Robert R. Bush[*] The marriage rules in certain primitive societies are designed to prevent marriage between close relatives, even when these relatives are not aware of the fact that they are related. This is desirable in a society where no exact records are kept and where family ties may soon be forgotten. The basic rule is that each person in the society is assigned a certain "marriage type" and that a man may marry a woman only if she is of his own type. Given the type of the parents, each son is assigned one definite type and each daughter is assigned another definite type.

We immediately see that brother-sister marriages are automatically forbidden in this society, since a son from a given marriage is always assigned a different type from that of a daughter.

Our basic set of objects is the set of marriage types. Our transformations will be rules according to which we find the type of a relative of a person, knowing the type of the person. Since a relative of a relative is again a relative, the result of applying two transformations will again be a transformation. Furthermore, if there is a transformation changing the type of an uncle to that of a nephew, there should also be a transformation that changes the type of a

[*] An improved treatment of the same model may be found in J. G. Kemeny, J. L. Snell, and G. L. Thompson, *Introduction to Finite Mathematics* (Englewood Cliffs, N.J.: Prentice-Hall, Inc., 1957), Chapter VII, Sections 7 and 8.

nephew to that of an uncle, and hence both conditions are satisfied for having a group of transformations.

Among the conditions of reasonableness for marriage types, the two most important conditions not yet mentioned are: "For any two individuals it is permissible for some of their descendants to intermarry"; and "The rule as to whether a man is allowed to marry a female relative of a given kind depends only on the kind of relationship." The former assures that the society does not split into castes, and the latter assures that there is no discrimination against a given marriage type.

We now have a mathematical model for marriage rules in primitive societies, and we may search the mathematical literature for appropriate theorems applicable to this problem. The basic result is that the marriage group must be a regular permutation group which is generated by the parent-to-son transformation and by the parent-to-daughter transformation. Since regular permutation groups are relatively rare, this theorem enables one to find easily all possible marriage rules for a given number of marriage types. For example, it is shown that there are but six possible sets of rules for a society having four marriage types. It is then interesting to note that two of these are actually in use in the Tarau and the Kariera societies respectively.

For example, in the Kariera society, the parent-to-son transformation interchanges types 1, 2, and 3, 4, whereas the parent-to-daughter transformation reverses the order of the types (see the following table). If we have parents of type 2, a son will have type 4, and his daughters will have type 1. A daughter of the original parents will have type 3, and her sons will also have type 1. Hence a son of a daughter of given parents will be allowed to marry a daughter of a son. The same is true no matter what type the grandparents are.

TYPE NUMBERS IN KARIERA SOCIETY

Parents	Son	Daughter
1	3	4
2	4	3
3	1	2
4	2	1

The model also suggests certain additional questions one may not have thought of in an informal formulation of the problem. For example, both the above-mentioned societies allow certain first-cousin marriages, though other first-cousin marriages are forbidden. It would be reasonable to impose an additional restriction that first-cousin marriages should always be forbidden. In this case one can prove that the necessary and sufficient condition for this is that parent-to-son and parent-to-daughter transformations should not commute and that their squares should not be equal. These additional conditions eliminate all regular groups with less than six types. Therefore we find that the Kariera and Tarau societies could not possibly have eliminated all first-cousin marriages if they wanted to use only four types.

This example is historically very interesting and illuminating. It is most impressive that a society that is unable to keep precise records should have been able to solve, through trial and error, a problem that requires fairly intricate mathematical operations for formal analysis. It also shows, however, that their procedures could have been considerably improved if they had been in a position to use modern algebra to design the rules. For example, they could have eliminated all first-cousin marriages.

We have just considered models in which numbers are not used and in which no geometry occurs. Now we shall consider others in which numbers or geometric concepts are artificially introduced: Model No. 3 will be numerical and Model No. 4 geometrical.

MODEL NO. 3

Let us consider a communication network. By this we mean a set of people with certain means of sending messages from one to the other. For each pair of people i and j it may be possible to send a message from i to j, from j to i, in both directions, or in neither direction. It would at first appear that this is a situation in which no numbers could ever be usefully introduced. However, a simple numerical model for communication networks has proved fruitful.

We introduce a square array of numbers, known as a matrix, which has as many rows and columns as there are people in our network. Let us call this matrix C and let us call the entry in the ith row and the jth column $c_{i,j}$; $c_{i,j}$ will be chosen to be 1 if it is possible to send a message directly from i to j; otherwise $c_{i,j} = 0$. In particular, we will always choose $c_{i,i} = 0$, which is merely a convention. (That is, by definition, a person cannot send himself a message.)

It is immediately clear that all the information available to us about the communication network is furnished by the matrix. However, any number of other methods could be thought of that would represent this information just as well. Has anything been gained by introducing numbers? Numbers are truly useful only if arithmetical operations are introduced. For example, matrices can be multiplied; in particular, we can multiply the matrix C by itself. According to the customary rules of matrix multiplication, we will then find that the entry in the ith row in the jth column of the new matrix will give us the number of different ways in which i can send a message to j in two steps.

In Fig. 3 we show communication matrix C for a network of four people in which 1 can communicate directly with 2, 2 can communicate directly with all three of the others, 3 can communicate directly with 4, and 4 can communicate directly with 1 and 3. We also show in the same figure C^2, which indicates the number of ways a given man can communicate with other men in two steps. For example, 2 can communicate with each man in two steps in just one way.

$$C = \begin{Bmatrix} 0 & 1 & 0 & 0 \\ 1 & 0 & 1 & 1 \\ 0 & 0 & 0 & 1 \\ 1 & 0 & 1 & 0 \end{Bmatrix} \qquad C^2 = \begin{Bmatrix} 1 & 0 & 1 & 1 \\ 1 & 1 & 1 & 1 \\ 1 & 0 & 1 & 0 \\ 0 & 1 & 0 & 1 \end{Bmatrix}$$

Figure 3

The fruitfulness of such a model might of course be judged in terms of theorems that can be proved about it. An interesting theorem* concerns a *complete* communication network. By this we mean that, for each pair of people i and j, it is possible to send a message either from i to j, or from j to i, or in both directions. For such a complete communication network there is a simple interpretation for having the largest number of ones in a given row. For example, in Fig. 3 (which shows a complete network) man 2 has the largest row sum, namely 3. The proof shows that the person whose row in the matrix has the largest row sum can communicate with everyone in the network in one or two steps. Of course, in Fig. 3 man 2 can actually do this in a single step.

This system has an interesting mathematical feature known as duality—namely, by interchanging rows and columns it is possible to change a matrix of "can send a message to" to a matrix of "can

---

* This theorem is proved in J. G. Kemeny, J. L. Snell, and G. L. Thompson, *op. cit.*, Chapter VII, Section 2.

receive a message from." The preceding theorem is still applicable to the dual matrix, and hence we know that if a given person's column sum is a maximum, then this person can receive a message from everybody in one or two steps. In our example, columns 1, 3, and 4 all have maximal column sum 2, and hence all three of these men can be reached by any man in one or two steps.

These results do not appear very surprising when there are only four men in our network; but when we consider a complex network of a hundred people, they may be very useful indeed. For example, an efficiency expert studying a large firm may find a communication matrix a convenient means for representing either the communication system or the table of organization of the company. Should he find that the company forms a complete communication network, he could immediately search for the hub of command from which instructions can be given in one or two steps to any employee. And even if the network is incomplete, studying powers of the communication matrix would provide valuable information.

This example illustrates in very simple terms how numerical tools may be introduced in a problem where no numbers are apparent. Our final model will show how geometrical tools may sometimes be useful in a problem that at first appears completely non-geometrical.

MODEL NO. 4

The problem confronting us deals with the ranking of a set of objects. Suppose that ten experts are each asked to rank a set of 50 objects, in order of preference. To allow a maximum amount of freedom, we will allow ties in the rankings. We are then supposed to arrive at a consensus ranking. How are we to do this? This problem can be reduced to a problem analogous to classical statistics problems[*] if we are able to introduce a measure of distance between rankings. So our problem is that of taking the set of all possible rankings of 50 objects and of turning them into a geometrical space, one in which a definite distance is defined between any two rankings. I will here summarize the results of some as yet unpublished research.[†]

Let us agree on some notation. We will have in mind a fixed

---

[*] See J. G. Kemeny, "Generalized Random Variables," *Pacific Journal* (1959).
[†] See J. G. Kemeny and J. L. Snell, *Mathematical Models in the Social Sciences* (Boston: Ginn & Company, 1962), Ch. 2.

number of objects to be ranked. We will denote by capital letters, A, B, C, etc., possible rankings. For example, if we have three objects, a, b, and c, in mind, then A may be the ranking where b is first, a is second, and c is third; and B may be the ranking where c is first and a and b are tied for second place. We want to introduce a measure of distance between pairs A and B, which will be denoted by $d(A, B)$. Let us try to agree on certain conditions that such a definition must satisfy.

Condition 1. d must satisfy the conditions for a distance laid down by a geometer. That is:

1. $d(A, B) \geq 0$, and equality holds if, and only if, A and B are the same ranking.
2. $d(A, B) = d(B, A)$.
3. $d(A, B) + d(B, C) \geq d(A, C)$, and the equality holds if, and only if, the ranking B is between A and C.

For the last part of condition 1, we need a definition of "betweenness." We will define betweenness in terms of pairwise judgments—that is, we will say that ranking B is *between* A and C if for each pair of objects, i and j, the judgment of B is between that of A and C. In other words, for the given pair the judgment of B either agrees with A or agrees with C, or A prefers i, C prefers j, and B declares them to be tied.

Next we must assure that our measure of distance does not in any way depend on the particular objects we have chosen for our rankings.

Condition 2. The definition of the distance d should not be affected by a relabeling of the set of objects to be ranked.

This means, for example, that if A rates three objects in the order a, b, c, and B rates them in the order c, b, a, the distance between these two rankings should be the same as the distance between the ranking b, c, a and a, c, b, since the latter may be obtained from the former by changing a to b, b to c, and c to a.

Condition 3. If the two rankings are in complete agreement at the beginning of the list and at the end of the list, and differ only as to the ranking of k objects in the middle, then this distance is the same as if these k objects were the only objects under consideration.

This condition is self-explanatory. Our final condition is in the nature of a convention. It may be thought of as choosing a unit of measurement.

Condition 4. The minimum positive distance is 1.

Let us suppose that we have agreed that these are four reasonable conditions for the definition of a distance between rankings. We have then translated our scientific problem into a purely mathematical problem. We can ask a mathematician three questions: (1) Is there any distance that will satisfy all of these conditions? Or, in other words, are our conditions consistent? (2) How can we characterize all definitions that will satisfy these four conditions? (3) What additional assumptions can we make that would narrow the possible choice from many distances to one?

In this particular case we are confronted with a pleasant surprise, in that we find that our conditions are indeed consistent, and that there is one and only one possible definition of distance which will satisfy all of these conditions. Therefore, if we have agreed on the four conditions above, we must agree that this is *the* correct definition of a distance. The details of this proof are here omitted.

The resulting distance may be described as follows. Compare the rankings A and B for each pair of individuals i and j. If the two rankings agree, we write down 0. If one prefers i to j and the other j to i, we write down 2. And if one expresses a preference while the other indicates a tie, we write down 1. Once we have these numbers written down for all pairs i and j, $d(A, B)$ equals the sum of these numbers.

Had we written down this definition to start with, we might have thought it a fairly reasonable way to measure the distance between two rankings. However, had other equally reasonable-sounding definitions been suggested, we would have had no rational way of choosing among them. With our present procedure the argument is reduced to the four conditions stated above. Anyone who accepts those four conditions *must* accept the resulting definition of d. Hence, anyone who rejects our definition of a distance must specify which of our conditions he rejects, and should be forced to give conditions of his own which are reasonable and which lead to a unique choice of the distance function. In this way an argument about a sociological problem can be put on a useful plane.

As an illustration, we show in Fig. 4 the possible rankings of three objects and the distances between these rankings. The notation used is such that

$$\left\{ \begin{array}{c} a \\ b - c \end{array} \right\}$$

indicates that a is in first place, b and c are tied for second place. Distances between neighboring rankings are indicated in the figure. Thus, for example, the (shortest) distance between

$$\begin{Bmatrix} a \\ b \\ c \end{Bmatrix} \quad \text{and} \quad (a - b - c) \text{ is } 1 + 2 = 3.$$

If we now ask a number of experts to rank three objects, we may use Fig. 4 to find the consensus ranking. This ranking may be defined as the one such that the sum of its distances from the various

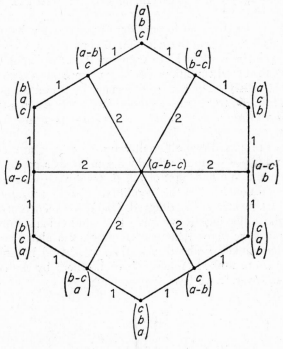

Figure 4

experts' rankings should be a minimum. Alternatively, it is sometimes convenient to take the sum of the squares of the distances to be a minimum. This would mean, for example, that if we have three experts, two of whom hand in the ranking, a, b, c, and one the ranking b, a, c, then the method of minimizing the sums of the distances will give a, b, c as the consensus ranking, while the method of minimizing the sum of squares of distances will yield a tie between a and b, with c a definite third. However, if there is considerable disagreement among the three experts—if, for example, the first one rates a, b, c in that order; the second one b, c, a; and the third one c, a, b—then the method of minimizing the sums of the squares of the distances will tell us that the consensus ranking is a three-way tie. The method of minimizing the sums of the distances, however, will give us three possible consensus rankings, namely, the three rankings given by the individual judges.

It is an essential feature of either of these methods that it always yields us at least one possible consensus ranking; but, as illustrated above, it may yield us more than one consensus. These basic tools enable one to carry out a certain amount of statistical work on rankings by experts.

An interesting question to consider is the relation between this definition of distance and the selection of consensus rankings on the one hand, and the work of K. J. Arrow on the other hand.

Arrow considered conditions that any reasonable system of social choice must satisfy.[*] His major result may be stated, in our terminology, as follows: *there is no method of selecting a consensus ranking from arbitrary sets of individual rankings that satisfies all his conditions.*

We have proposed two different ways of arriving at a consensus ranking, and hence we must ask how our methods escaped from the Arrow theorem. We find, first of all, that we have violated one of his basic conditions. This is the "condition of irrelevant alternatives," which has frequently been criticized. One consequence of this condition is the following: if we have three individuals ranking our objects, and if we know that two have ranked a ahead of b while the third has ranked b ahead of a, then we should be able to tell how a and b are ranked (relative to each other) by the consensus ranking. However, if we have two rankings

$$\left\{ \begin{array}{c} a \\ c \\ b \end{array} \right\}$$

and one of

$$\left\{ \begin{array}{c} b \\ a \\ c \end{array} \right\}$$

[*] See K. J. Arrow, *Social Choice and Individual Values* (New York: John Wiley & Sons, Inc., 1951).

our consensus ranking the method of squares will be

$$\left\{ \begin{array}{c} a \\ b-c \end{array} \right\}$$

Whereas if two individuals arrive at the ranking

$$\left\{ \begin{array}{c} a \\ b \\ c \end{array} \right\}$$

and the third at

$$\left\{ \begin{array}{c} b \\ c \\ a \end{array} \right\}$$

then the consensus will be

$$\left\{ \begin{array}{c} a-b \\ c \end{array} \right\}.$$

In the former case a is preferred to b by the consensus, while in the latter they are tied. When we examine these two situations on Fig. 4, they appear exactly alike, and it is hard to see why anyone would disagree with the consensus rankings. This lends further evidence to the thesis that the condition of irrelevant alternatives should be rejected.

But there is a second and more basic way in which our methods differ from those investigated by Arrow, namely, that we occasionally arrive at multiple consensus rankings. We conclude that the requirement of a unique social ordering is too restrictive. It suffices that we should arrive at a unique ordering "in most cases."

CONCLUSION

The four models discussed above illustrate various ways in which mathematics may be useful in nonnumerical and nonspatial problems in the social sciences. They illustrate how both modern algebra and modern geometry provide new techniques for these fields, and they show that these techniques may apply in situations where numbers and space are never introduced or where numbers and space are more or less artificially introduced into nonmathematical problems.

Of particular importance is the method illustrated in the fourth model. Often social scientists may be in agreement on requirements for the solution of a certain problem, even when no agreement can be reached on an actual solution. In such cases a mathematician should be consulted. He may show them that it is impossible to meet all the requirements they have laid down, and in that case they would have to agree on ways of asking for less. Or, very likely, he may tell them that there are infinitely many ways of solving their problem, and give them some indication of the kind of additional requirements they could make on a solution. Finally, in an ideal situation such as the one illustrated in Model No. 4, he may be able to prove that there is a unique solution to the problem they have laid down. In this case he would solve, once and for all, a hitherto unresolved problem, and would provide the social scientist with a most useful tool for his work.

PART II EDUCATION

8 THE SECONDARY SCHOOL CURRICULUM

Recently, national attention has been focused on the high school curriculum, and many worthwhile suggestions for its improvement have emerged. But I question the very starting point of this debate: is the high school a natural unit of education?

In the United States we are used to educational systems which are divided in an 8-4 or a 6-3-3 pattern. Under the former the serious education of students starts in ninth grade, while under the latter usually only in the tenth grade. In many European countries the division is 4-8, with gymnasium education starting at age 10. Although I feel that 10 is too young an age, I also feel that 14 or 15 is too late. I am quite certain that the junior high school is a major cause of the fact that American school children fall behind their European contemporaries.

To my mind 6-6 is an ideal division. The primary school serves to teach basic skills, to get students used to school work, and to develop good study habits. A child should be ready for the serious business of education by the beginning of seventh grade. Therefore, this essay addresses itself to the secondary school curriculum, thought of as a single unit.

First we must consider what constitutes a reasonable load for the children. If by a full unit we mean a course that meets for 50 minutes a day, five days a week, throughout the academic year, then I feel that at the very least we should require four units in grades seven and eight, and five units thereafter. These units should be in addition to such non-academic activities as gym and driver training, and they should require a substantial amount of homework, which increases steadily.

I am addressing myself to the students who might go to college. This is a significantly larger group than the group that does go to college, and more easily identifiable at age 14. It is a great mistake to limit college-prep courses to those who will almost surely go to college. It does no harm to have a student complete the more demanding curriculum and then decide to quit after high school. But eliminating a possible college student through the wrong selection, at age 14, is a crime.

It may be argued that no national standards can be set, owing to the variations of state requirements. But this is not really true. While state requirements vary tremendously, they set only minimum standards, and any good college preparatory course-sequence will meet (with very minor changes) the requirements of all states. These curricula are far more influenced by the demands of leading colleges than by state requirements.

James B. Conant's famous report did a great service to the nation in calling our attention to scandalous shortcomings of the national standard of high school education, and in recommending a minimum standard for all schools. Although much of what he says will be praised by any educator, I find myself in basic disagreement with Mr. Conant on one major issue.

Mr. Conant is an advocate of a minimal core curriculum, with programs of students arranged on an individual basis, allowing a maximum number of electives. After a great deal of thought I have come to the opposite conclusion. I favor a uniform core curriculum, covering most of the secondary school program for the "college-capable student," with a minimum number of electives.

My basic reason for this is that the average high school student is in no position to make sensible use of so much freedom. Nor do I believe that counselors can solve the problem. A good counselor will give sound advice on how to achieve a specified goal, but the difficulty is precisely that the 14-year-old student is extremely vague about his goals. I have advised college students for more than a dozen years, and the one lesson that I have learned is that most college students change their goals in college. Therefore, the only intelligent procedure is to leave all major fields open until the time is ripe for the student to choose his career.

An extremely flexible system of electives is also very costly, and leads to difficulties in scheduling. Few schools are large enough and rich enough to be able to offer a full set of electives and at the same time group students according to their ability. And to my mind, ability grouping is the most important feature of secondary education.

In another essay ("The Mathematically Talented Student") I expressed my views on this matter, as far as mathematics is concerned. Similar arguments are completely convincing in all fields. Instead of allowing students to drop a subject that is at the moment distasteful, or whose usefulness is not immediately obvious, encourage each student to proceed at his fastest pace in the fields he likes best (and is best qualified in), and allow him to proceed at a normal or slow pace in other subjects.

One final remark of a general nature is in order. The American high school is strangled by the requirement that all courses must meet five times a week. I see no reason why half courses shouldn't be offered. These could be scheduled in a variety of ways: they could meet Mondays, Wednesdays, and alternate Fridays, with other half courses filling the vacated days. Or they could meet Monday-Wednesday-Friday for half the year and Tuesday-Thursday for the other half. Or some courses could meet two days a week while others met three times. For example, seventh graders could take a language course on Tuesdays and Thursdays, while eighth graders elected the course on the other three days. That way the same language teacher could teach four or five sections of seventh grade language *and* of eighth graders. She would prepare for only one age level on any given day.

With these preliminary remarks I am ready to sketch a secondary school curriculum. Needless to say, many variations are possible, and many improvements will occur to the reader. Therefore, I recommend only the spirit of the following remarks, not necessarily the details.

It is generally agreed that a student should carry six years of English. This is certainly desirable, and one would hope that by the end of 12th grade each student has thoroughly mastered the ability to read and write good English, and has become acquainted with a fair sample of English literature. Unfortunately, this is rarely the case.

To a great extent the fault lies with the English language. Its grammar is so disorderly, and its spelling so illogical, that English-speaking students must spend an unreasonable portion of their time mastering their own language. It seems to me that the time has come to shed all the restrictions placed on us by historical accident, and simplify the English language. I can think of no project that would improve American education more quickly than a national effort to agree to a simplified spelling and grammar.

I am particularly conscious of this fact, since Hungarian—my native language—is essentially phonetic. As a result of this, it was expected that a fifth grade student would never make a spelling error. This requirement sounds utopian in English, but is entirely reasonable in Hungarian. As a result, Hungarian children spend the last eight years of their Hungarian classes in studying literature and in improving their ability to write.

This may be an appropriate place to express a deep conviction: I do not believe that education must be dreadfully boring to be good for the soul. Nor do I believe that all that is old is worthwhile.

In the cross section of literature taught in high school, it is desirable to include Shakespeare and Keats to represent the classics, but Shaw and Hemingway are also excellent examples of literature, and may be more meaningful to the students. There is no excuse for inflicting *Silas Marner* on a teen-ager.

Social studies is probably the most neglected field in the curriculum. It is important to understand our civilization and its history. And, while I agree that each nation should know its own history and government particularly well, I regret the tendency that limits the social studies of most American students to American history and government. The world is too small and too closely knit to allow this isolationist attitude.

I advocate some required social studies throughout the six years. The following might be a reasonable grade sequence: (7th) *American history and government*. Since this course builds on several years of grade-school background, it could be more than the usual "civics" course. (8th) *Ancient and medieval history*. It is time that we admitted that history began before Columbus discovered America. (9th) *Modern history*. And I have in mind a course that has some world perspective. It is perfectly true that today the United States is the center of the civilized world. But this was certainly not true in the eighteenth century, and I deplore courses that teach history purely from a U.S.-centric point of view. (10th) *Geography*. I list this course later than customary, to allow it to be a serious course dealing with economic and social problems, rather than a catalogue of uninteresting and indigestible facts. To fit into my over-all scheme of the number of units required (see p. 87), I would settle for a half unit here. (11th) *American history*, on a level now taught to college freshmen. (12th) *Contemporary problems*, both in the U.S. and in the rest of the world.

Since much of this volume is devoted to the teaching of mathematics, I shall limit myself to a list of courses. I am assuming that the present reforms have taken place, and hence in five years we can teach more than in the traditional six-year secondary curriculum: (7th) *Real number system*. Granted the improvements now being made in grade school, and eliminating the usual junior high junk, we should be able to conclude our treatment of the real numbers in seventh grade. (8th) *First year algebra*. (9th) *Geometry plane and solid*, with some analytic geometry. (10th) *Second year algebra*, including trigonometry and the connection of algebra to geometry. (11th) A half unit of *probability* and *statistics*. (12th) A half unit on *analytics* and *elementary functions*. The student completing this unit should be ready to start college mathematics with calculus.

In recent years much progress has been made in developing a more modern and more demanding science sequence for high schools. This must now be supplemented by a change in attitude, according to which it is part of general intelligence and culture to have a nodding acquaintance with the major sciences. I would therefore consider the following $3\frac{1}{2}$ units as minimal: (8th) A half unit of *geology* and *astronomy*. (9th) *Biology*. (10th) *Chemistry*. (11th) *Physics*.

I shall return to mathematics and science when I discuss electives.

This brings me to the subject of foreign languages. I have learned through sad experience, as a member of the Hanover, N.H., school board, that no other topic is quite as emotionally charged as this one. I shall propose a compromise that will meet the requirements of colleges and the needs of future scientists. But I am quite sure that it will be bitterly attacked from all sides.

There are many arguments in favor of studying foreign languages. They are asserted to help us understand our own language; they help us in foreign travel, they bring us closer to other civilizations, and they open up wide areas of literature. I am quite sure that these arguments are basically sound, and I fully agree that each college-capable student should master one foreign language. But this leads to the root of the controversy. Shall it be ancient or modern? Shall it be one or two languages? How much time should be devoted to it?

First of all, we must decide whether to cross the Rubicon. Should our students study Latin? I for one firmly oppose this. Let me consider the usual arguments advanced by the small but very vocal group of advocates of Latin, and try to answer them.

We are told that studying Latin helps in learning other foreign languages. This is no doubt true. But I seriously doubt that two years of Latin followed by three years of French will be as successful *in teaching French* as five years of French. We are told that Latin helps us to understand English. But so does French, and probably more so. We are told that many students get their only acquaintance with ancient history through Latin. That may regrettably be true, and I therefore advocate a full unit on ancient and medieval history. But I studied Latin for $3\frac{1}{2}$ years, and the amount of ancient history I managed to dig out of this could be taught much less painfully, in English, in half a year.

In the last analysis the advocates of Latin are traditionalists who like to see their children follow in their own footsteps. But modern civilization is too full and too complex to allow the luxury of this eighteenth-century ideal. I am in favor of electives in Latin for the small minority, but the majority should concentrate on a contemporary foreign language.

The same argument applies to the study of two languages. Although this is desirable, so is the study of six years of science, of much more history, etc. One must compromise; one contemporary foreign language thoroughly mastered is the best we can hope for with the majority of students. At the moment even this limited goal is rarely achieved.

The choice of the language is much easier. There are many reasons why French, German, or Russian recommend themselves. All three are spoken by many millions of people with whom we have close contacts. All three languages have given rise to a rich and varied literature. And although French and German are more directly helpful in understanding English, and are easier to learn, for the good student there is an extra challenge in learning a drastically different language.

Although I recognize the practical value and popularity of Spanish, I must advise caution. Not only is the Spanish literature more limited, but there is a danger for the future scientist. I have seen too many promising scientists who enter college with Latin or Spanish as their only language, and who must devote a major fraction of their college studies to languages. Graduate schools of science require a reading knowledge of two foreign languages, and it is very important that a student acquire one of these in high school. French and German are the leading scientific languages of the past, and English and Russian are the scientific languages of the future. For all these reasons, the student is best advised to concentrate on French, German, or Russian. And since few students know at age 12 whether they will become scientists, this is sound advice for any student.

Finally, we must face the question of how early languages should be started, and how long they should be studied. Here we are confronted by two opposing, but equally valid, arguments. There is overwhelming evidence that it is easier to start a language at a young age. This would indicate that the foreign language should be started in seventh grade. But we want to be sure of a reading (and if possible speaking) knowledge of the language when college is entered. This argues for continuing the language through twelfth grade. Many freshmen who could easily have passed their

	7	8	9	10	11	12
English	1	1	1	1	1	1
Social studies	American history and government	Ancient and medieval history	Modern history	Geography $\frac{1}{2}$	American history	Contemporary problems
Mathematics	Numbers	Algebra	Geometry	Algebra and trigonometry	Probability and statistics $\frac{1}{2}$	Elementary functions $\frac{1}{2}$
Science		Geology and astronomy $\frac{1}{2}$	Biology	Chemistry	Physics	
Foreign language	$\frac{1}{2}$	$\frac{1}{2}$	$\frac{1}{2}$	1	1	1
Other	Shop or home economics $\frac{1}{2}$		Elective $\frac{1}{2}$	Elective $\frac{1}{2}$	Elective $\frac{1}{2}$	Elective $1\frac{1}{2}$
Total units	4	4	5	5	5	5

college's language requirement after tenth grade have forgotten their fundamentals in two years.

Therefore, one group advocates six full years of a language (not to mention those who would carry it through from third grade). But experience shows that the majority of students elect at most four years, and that they are quite well qualified at the end of this period. I would therefore like to suggest a simple compromise: have the foreign language started in seventh grade, but carry only half units for the first three years. And carry full units of the language in grades 10–12, when the literature will be most meaningful. Thus the student would take $4\frac{1}{2}$ units over a period of six years.

Let us add to this the usual seventh grade requirement of shop or home economics, and we have completed the core curriculum. I have summarized this in the chart on p. 87.

We note that although electives are far from abundant, there is some room for electives in the last four years. Some of these, especially in grades 9 or 10, may be used to acquire a knowledge of typing (extremely useful in college and later life), or to elect a remedial reading course. The rest should be used to concentrate in the student's field of major interest.

For example, a student interested in mathematics and science could complete the two half units of mathematics in the eleventh grade, and take college-level courses in calculus and one of the sciences in his senior year. Naturally, this is desirable only if the school has a qualified teacher. I am afraid this is rarely the case today. Another attractive half-unit elective could be a course in the fundamentals of computing machines.

The student who is oriented towards the humanities or social sciences might be attracted by introductory psychology, or an additional literature course, or a senior elective in philosophy. While the student who is tremendously interested in languages (or whose parents insist on a knowledge of Latin) could use the electives to study a second foreign language.

I do not feel that this curriculum is the ultimate answer to all our problems. However, it does present some advantages. It is easier to administer than a system full of electives. It would assure that our students have acquired at least a basic knowledge of various facets of our civilization, and it would serve as useful preparation for the student, no matter what his eventual choice of a career may turn out to be.

9 THE WELL-ROUNDED MAN vs. THE EGGHEAD *

An accidental by-product of the great growth of the American population has been that good liberal arts colleges have had considerable freedom in choosing their freshman classes. In the not too distant past all sufficiently well-to-do students were admitted, and scholarship funds were used to attract exceptionally able students from less well-to-do families. Recently colleges have been embarrassed by their riches. This has in many instances led to a serious re-examination of the principles on which students are accepted and rejected.

Although any such statement is necessarily an oversimplification, it is fair to say that the faculties of Ivy League schools are arguing for more bright students while the administration and alumni bodies are looking for the "well-rounded man." It is this heated argument that has suggested the title for the present essay.

The ideal candidate for our Ivy League college is a boy from a small midwestern town, where he was first in his graduating class, an all-state football player, an Eagle Scout, president of his senior class, and winner of the annual prize in Latin. He splits his spare time evenly between good literature, playing the flute, and running a small corporation which he organized himself. Presumably such a student would make both the admissions office and the faculty extremely happy, but for some reason such candidates are hard to find. Whereas our admissions officers at Ivy League schools accuse the faculty of being willing to admit a very bright but exceedingly dull and unenterprising student, the faculty claims that the admissions office would be satisfied with the above qualifications even if high grades and reading good literature were omitted from the list.

I would be interested in having a psychologist prepare an ac-

* Copyright by *The New York Times*. Reprinted by permission. First appeared in *The New York Times Magazine*, April, 1962, under the title "Needed: The Well-rounded College."

curate composite picture of the egghead as seen by the alumni of one of our distinguished educational institutions. He is likely to be tall and gangling, to wear thick glasses, to stutter, and to have an absent-minded expression on his face. He always carries several books, and is too involved to "get the most out of college." He is likely to contribute only nuclear physics or philosophy to the dormitory bull session, and he is too busy to show up at a football rally before the Harvard game. Although he is likely to obtain a Phi Beta Kappa key in his senior year, his inherent shyness will prevent him from becoming a success in life. He may be well qualified to become a college professor, but he will not amount to anything.

By contrast, the faculty pictures the well-rounded man as muscular and jovial, constantly slapping his fellow students on the back. Although he may attend classes when he is not out of town playing hockey, he is too busy debating or running the undergraduate council or singing in the Glee Club to do more than a minimum necessary amount of studying. He is likely to be at a fraternity party in preference to writing an honors thesis, and will switch his radio in the evening from a string quartet to some currently popular jazz. He will graduate with a gentleman's C— average, and may later become a business executive or a senator, but he will not make a worthwhile contribution to civilization.

I should first like to say a few words in favor of the alumni side of this debate. It is certainly true that if we populated our campuses with the grotesque caricatures of eggheads visualized by the old grads, our colleges and universities would be most unhealthy places. It is also to be admitted that in our modern complex civilization the extremely brilliant and completely one-sided man is a menace. We do not want such a person in a position of leadership, and insofar as our institutions hope to train the leaders of tomorrow, they are well advised to pick better raw material. There is also the danger of such an extreme intellectual turning neurotic, and since neuroses are socially contagious, colleges are wise in being wary of potential neurotics. However, once this has been said, the well-worn argument in favor of more well-rounded students seems to go to pieces.

It is my conviction that over a period of 100 years a fundamentally sound goal has been distorted into a ludicrous caricature of the original. I am a firm believer in the *well-rounded college* as an atmosphere in which an intellectual should study. But somehow, through a most unfortunate semantic accident, the emphasis has been transferred from the well-rounded college to the well-rounded man.

It is a wonderfully stimulating experience to spend four years in an academic environment in which even the most esoteric thirst can be quenched. My own taste ran from mathematics and physics, through philosophy, to literature, psychology, and economics. I had no particular interest in biology as a whole, but I was fascinated by genetics, and I certainly appreciated having an outstanding geneticist on the campus. I am quite sure that I did not begin to tap the wonderfully varied resources of Princeton University, but it was a great source of pride and satisfaction for me to know that these resources were available. Although I have never had the temptation to read Plato in the original, it was nice to know that if I were ever so tempted I would have someone around who could help me. I have never personally found rock formations fascinating, but I was glad that my friends could have their geological questions answered by experts. I have never quite had the time to spare to study the abnormal psychology of South Sea Islanders, but I found it a considerable comfort to know that an irresistible urge to delve into this field would not be frustrated.

It was stimulating to be surrounded by students from all over the world, whose tastes and interests varied considerably from my own, and to find the very same issues being discussed by men with such varying backgrounds, interests and abilities. Later, as a member of the faculty, both at Princeton and Dartmouth, I found discussions with my colleagues incomparably stimulating for the same reasons. This to my mind is the justification for the well-rounded college.

The argument that the well-rounded college should consist of well-rounded students is a non sequitur. I will try to argue that it is neither necessary to have our colleges and universities stocked with well-rounded students, nor is it desirable to have them around in large numbers. After all, if it were necessary or desirable to have the students well-rounded wouldn't it be even more important to have well-rounded faculty members? This would lead to staffing our institutions with intellectual dilettantes who have a *Reader's Digest* knowledge of a wide variety of different fields.

When I became fascinated with the philosophy of Plato, I most needed on campus an expert in Plato. Had I exhausted my professor's knowledge within one semester, it would have been very little comfort to me that he was also widely read in Economics, or that he was an amateur astronomer, or even that he was a first rate pianist. I appreciated faculty members with a breadth of interest who could guide me in the terrifying mazes of twentieth-century knowledge, but above all, I wanted them to be experts in some major field of human undertaking.

The picture of a university stocked with well-rounded students, whose sole aim is to acquire a maximum of breadth without giving in to the temptation of specialization, is a nightmare. It brings to mind a curriculum in which no course is numbered above 2, and where a faculty member must spend most of his life introducing completely ignorant students to some new era of temporary intellectual interest. Unlike many other mathematicians, I have always enjoyed teaching freshmen. But one of my principal motivations has always been to kindle the flame that will drive the student to a serious exploration of advanced mathematics.

I too have enjoyed participating in debating societies and theater groups, and although I have never been particularly good at athletics, I am an ardent fan. These are pleasant pastimes when used to relax after a fruitful day's work. But the thought of letting loose on the country leaders whose primary interest is in these activities frightens me. I would much rather have the country governed by men who use every spare moment to read (and if possible write) books, than those who think the day's work as time taken away from playing golf or reading westerns.

We are told that it is good to have well-rounded men on the campus because this leads to a stimulating surrounding for students. This may be true in a sense, but it is the stimulation of a cocktail party. It leads to conversations in which each person freely lets off undigested ideas on a variety of relatively shallow topics, knowing that there is no one present who knows enough to challenge him. It leads to an emphasis on sports and other extracurricular activities to the point where we have become a nation noted for the fact that in the majority of its universities these activities outweigh the importance of learning.

More fundamentally, we must ask if the man who knows a little about everything is really a well educated person. Certainly the so-called distributive requirements at most of our institutions aim precisely in this direction. I presume that these requirements are left over from that fortunate stage of civilization when it was possible for an intelligent person to have a good over-all view of human knowledge. Einstein once told me that when he was a young man he read everything that was written in physics. When he reached the age of seventy he could no longer keep up with everything that was being written about the Theory of Relativity. This was not due to the aging process, as Einstein was the hardest working 70-year-old I have ever met, but rather to the explosion in human knowledge that has been witnessed in the twentieth century. If we now find it impossible to keep up with everything that is being written in a single major area of human knowledge, how much is a man going to profit by trying to become knowledgeable in some two dozen different fields?

I remember an eloquent plea by one of my colleagues at Princeton University against an attempt to spread knowledge too thin. He pleaded for the man who sets himself the goal of becoming the world's outstanding expert in some small and narrow field of human undertaking, and devotes his entire life to scholarship and research in a single field. He argued that more understanding can be obtained by study in depth of one such field than by a smattering over a wide variety of different fields. Although I personally feel that this position is somewhat extreme, I do think that it has a major element of truth in it. I do not believe anyone can understand human civilization unless he has for a major period of life devoted himself to the effort of pursuing a subject deeply enough to reach the frontiers of human knowledge. I hope that there is time in human life to combine knowledge in depth with a sufficient broadening experience to be aware of several other major fields.

So far I have been talking in generalities. I hope now to make some practical suggestions as to how our liberal arts colleges can solve their problem of selecting freshmen in the age of too many outstanding applicants. I would propose a scheme in which each freshman class is carefully picked to be well-rounded, although individuals within the class are permitted to be specialists. As a matter of fact I would advocate that each student be picked for a specific trait, but that the class as a whole be well balanced. This would lead to a system of quotas.

First of all I would allow each academic department, or perhaps each major area of academic learning, to pick a specified number of students because of promise of excellence in their own field. This is of vital importance, because it is the presence of a few outstanding students in one's own field that makes teaching a truly rewarding profession.

Next I would allow a certain quota for the assurance that extracurricular activities are well stocked. Of course no student should be admitted unless he can meet certain minimum academic qualifications, but once these have been met, I see no harm in admitting the bright outstanding football player or the bright outstanding musician. I would think it much healthier for Ivy League schools

to admit frankly that certain students are accepted primarily because of their athletic prowess, than to continue the present
hypocrisy. I would also hope that in exchange for admitting an outstanding football player who promises to be a mediocre student, I
would be able to pick a promising mathematician, even if he has not
shown any particular interest in extracurricular activities.

I would next allow the alumni council to select some alumni
sons who are qualified for admission, but have not already been
picked. I recognize the value of tradition at Ivy League schools
and feel it worthwhile that we obtain a reasonable number of
qualified but not outstanding students to help develop loyalty to
one's alma mater. I would even be perfectly happy to have a small
number of students admitted primarily because their parents are
likely to be generous with us in the future.

One must recognize the fact that tuition pays only about half
the cost of educating a student and that all major colleges and
universities depend heavily on outside funds for maintaining high
standards. I see no harm in admitting a millionaire's son mainly
because he is a millionaire's son. He can pay for the education of a
hundred other students over a period of years. It should also not be
overlooked that he will have considerable influence on our civilization in the future, and we would like to see him well educated.

Next I would allow the admissions office to practice its favorite
games: It can pick a number of students mainly to assure healthy
geographic distribution. It can select others because of their promise
of leadership. And finally it should be allowed to admit a small
number of students whose record does not look so good, but the
admissions officers have a "hunch" that the students have greater
potential than has yet been realized. All of these factors are likely
to lead to an improvement in the well-roundedness of the college.

Finally I would like to see a small quota reserved for screwballs.
There is an increasing danger at leading schools that the possibility
of eliminating unorthodox students will lead to a degree of con-
formity highly dangerous to intellectual life. I should like to see
this counteracted by admitting in each class at least two dozen
men whose sole qualifications are that they are exceedingly bright
and of an unorthodox frame of mind.

The quota system might be implemented somewhat as follows:
First the admissions committee would process all applicants, eliminating any man clearly not qualified academically or suffering from
serious psychological or personality defects to make him unacceptable. Then this information should be turned over to a carefully selected faculty committee.

The faculty committee should be allowed to pick two-thirds of the freshman class. Presumably most of these students would be picked for all-around academic excellence. However a certain number of them would have to be selected for exceptional ability in a specialized field, while others would be selected because of particular interests. It is important to admit a small number of prospectively brilliant mathematicians and scientists even if they have shown a tendency to neglect other academic subjects, and it is just as important to admit a future poet or novelist even if his mathematical aptitude score is regrettably low. One must also recognize that, unless students with special interests in such fields as the creative arts or geology or anthropology are given preferential treatment, these fields are likely to die of intellectual starvation.

I would then allow five per cent quotas each for the picking of athletes, alumni sons, sons of well-to-do parents, students from far away geographic locations, prospective leaders, and those mysterious "hunches" of the admissions people. Relatively small quotas may be very valuable here, since these committees would know of several students in their own province who had already been accepted for academic reasons. That is, I am proposing that alumni be allowed to pick five per cent of the freshman class, in addition to those alumni sons who were academically outstanding. The remaining few places in the freshman class should then be filled with the best available professional screwballs.

I am quite sure that this plan, if ever implemented, would make all interest groups—including the faculty—extremely happy. It is a pity that by the very nature of this plan it is impossible to implement it.

10 EDUCATION OF THE WELL-ROUNDED MAN

Now that we have gotten our egghead or our well-rounded high school student into college, what is likely to happen to him? At this point, the European and American universities will provide quite different answers.

In Europe a university is a place where a man learns a profession. He may go to the university to become a doctor, a lawyer, an engineer, a mathematician, or a historian. But he is supposed to have chosen a profession, and his general education is left to the gymnasium. His university curriculum will consist of courses designed for his specialty and of cognates directly or indirectly useful to his profession.

In the United States this role is reserved for the graduate school. The American liberal arts college (a category that includes the first four years of major universities) has a threefold purpose: (1) to continue the well-rounding; (2) to help a student in choosing a career; and (3) to qualify him for graduate school if his chosen career requires graduate training.

On the whole, I favor the American plan. Our civilization is so complex that graduate training is becoming a necessity for a surprisingly large number of college students. Hence, it is reasonable to design the undergraduate years to form a bridge between the sheltered and regimented life of high school and the complete freedom and narrow training of graduate institutions. One must also realize that, owing to the complexity of modern culture, the average high school graduate has little knowledge of what professions exist, and what type of work each involves. Hence we find that most college students modify their plans during their undergraduate years.

It is reasonable to carry part of a student's "liberal" training into college. This will increase both the breadth of his training and the depth of his understanding. A 20-year-old college student will find meaning in a Bernard Shaw play that would certainly have escaped him in high school at age 16.

But, while I accept the goals of the American liberal arts college, there is considerable doubt in my mind as to the means of carrying these goals out. Experts in liberal education continually complain that the demands of professions whittle away at the liberal arts experience. However, there is increasing discontent on the part of students with what remains of the liberal education. I do not worry about the choice of a profession and about preprofessional training at our colleges. The professions will enforce their own standards. But I want to take a careful look at how the college makes sure that the end product is well-rounded.

Let us begin by examining the plans at two typical liberal arts institutions, Cornover College and Western Waynsley.

Cornover College requires a two-year sequence in "All the Ideas of Man." The first year covers "The discovery of fire to the Copernican revolution," while the second year deals with "The circulation of the blood to nonrepresentational painting."

Although the course is geared to the nonexpert, high standards are maintained. Students work very hard in this course. One sophomore was in the infirmary for three days, and he missed the entire Renaissance. The only complaint about the course is that the grading depends somewhat on who reads the final examination. For example, to the question "What was Newton's greatest discovery?", Professor Jones expects the answer "The laws of motion," while Dr. Brown requires as an answer "The calculus."

Students come out of the course with a magnificent stock of cocktail party conversation pieces. They know some one fact about each of 100 famous men. They can speak an intelligent sentence about Athens, Roman Law, the Dark Ages, the Rise of Science, the Impressionists, and Relativity Theory. And a cocktail party rarely requires more than one sentence on any one subject.

Western Waynsley has a totally different approach to the problem of breadth in learning. No one course is required, but the student elects a number of basic introductory courses. For example, each student elects four science courses, from six departments, but no two from the same department. Thus the student may elect either invertebrate zoology or vertebrate zoology, but selecting both semesters constitutes specialization.

When one adds to these "distributive requirements" the requirements in English, in foreign languages, and prerequisites for a major, the student has filled his entire schedule for the first two years. Thus, except for his chosen major, the student is not allowed to progress beyond a course numbered 1 or 2 in any subject.

It is a very demanding task to design a suitable course, of one semester duration, which will give the nonexpert an over-all view of the field. And students are not always appreciative of these difficulties. For example, the two eligible psychology courses are nicknamed "Terminology 1 and 2." The very popular European history course is referred to as "Blood and Gore." Equally well-known are "Hamlet for the Illiterate," "Experiments that Should have Worked," and "Star-Gazing 2."

In selecting a college, a student should pay careful attention as to where psychology is classified. At Cornover College it is a science, and therefore a favorite means of social scientists fulfilling the science requirement. However, at Western Waynsley it is a social science, and therefore available to science students who need an A in a nonscience course.

Having talked to graduates of both these institutions, I have come to the conclusion that well-rounding should allow for more depth than at Waynsley, without the necessity of the universal knowledge course-sequence at Cornover.

I have listened to many academic debates on the distributive requirements. Most of the worry concerns the highly specialized scientist. Actually, the facts are nearly the reverse. Most science students take full advantage of the opportunity to elect nonscience courses, insofar as the heavy demands of their specialties allow. But most nonscience students elect a science course only when they are forced to.

This argument was brought to our attention dramatically by C. P. Snow. He makes an excellent case for a redefinition of what constitutes a well-rounded intellect. Is it reasonable to classify someone who knows literature and music and nothing else as cultured, while a scientist who may know a wide variety of different fields but has read relatively little classical literature is automatically narrow? Why is it unforgivable not to know of the works of Keats and Brahms, but perfectly acceptable not to have heard of Gauss and Euler, the two greatest mathematicians of all time?

The ideal of knowing a good deal about all major areas of human achievement is an admirable one. But it is an ideal of the age of Jefferson, and Mr. Jefferson may have been the last man to achieve it. Civilization has become much too complex for any one man to have even a nodding acquaintance with the major interests of modern man.

There are vast areas of human achievement. Mathematics, physical science, life science, medicine, engineering, law, literature, the arts, the social sciences, history, and philosophy all deserve attention by a man of broad intellect. But isn't he more likely to profit by concentrating on three or four of these fields rather than scattering his energies in a hopeless pursuit of universal knowledge?

Wouldn't it be more reasonable to present to the entering freshman some such list of major areas, and tell him that during his college career he must penetrate four fields to a reasonable depth? One of these would contain his chosen specialty, and a requirement of two or three years' study in each of three other areas would assure that he is sampling the fruits of modern civilization.

My own ideal would be to see a number of three-year course units available for nonspecialists, and force each student to work his way through three such units in addition to his preprofessional training. But this suggestion brings us in direct conflict with the present philosophy on "distributive" courses.

It seems to be an implicit assumption that a course in field X for a student specializing in non-X is inherently distasteful, and hence must be short and sweet. Many departments get their heaviest enrollments, and hence the major justification for their budget, from such distributive courses. They will, therefore, go to considerable trouble to maintain a high level of enrollment. It is not surprising that this often results in low standards and easy grading.

Many scientists, myself included, have complained that nonscience students are shockingly ignorant of even the simplest principle of science. I have argued that letting such students become leaders of the country (there is not one scientist in Congress!) is extremely dangerous. But recently I have received a thought-provoking letter from an able senior, which shed new light on the problem.

The student argued that he too is troubled by his ignorance of science. But he found his choices discouraging. There were the usual one-semester or one-year watered-down courses, which he felt did not achieve the purpose. And there were sequences designed for specialists which he could have elected. But the average social scientist with a sincere desire to learn science has to pay a high price for electing the professional sequence. To compete in a physics sequence with students who have chosen physics as their profession either requires a completely unreasonable effort, or results in very poor grades. The demands of the nonscientist's graduate school will make either alternative unacceptable. So the student settles for the usual short-and-easy survey courses, and resigns himself to ignorance of science.

Although I did manage to point out some exceptions to this general description of science courses, on the whole I think the senior is right. Nonscience students, no matter how well intentioned, see watered-down courses or professional sequences as the only alternatives.

There is an analogous, but slightly different, problem confronting the science student who wants to learn about the social sciences. He finds the introductory course too simple, and the professional sequences unpalatable. But he has an additional legitimate complaint. The introductory courses in the social sciences tend to be full of terminology hardly of any interest to the nonspecialist; and the theoretical parts of these courses proceed at snail's pace, in large part because the students are unused to following theoretical arguments and unable to use mathematics. The science student has every reason to believe that he could progress much more rapidly in a course specially designed for him.

I should like to make use of *this* forum to design the Kemeny Plan of Well-rounding (to be referred to henceforth as KPW). This may be a cowardly procedure, but it is much easier to sell KPW to my publisher than to do battle with all the vested interests of universities.

First of all, KPW will do away with the superstition that distributive requirements must correspond to the usual administrative divisions of a college (science, social science, and humanities). It is only the fact that college professors have learned to do battle through their academic divisions that leads to the well-accepted practice. It has never been clear to me how a geology course was a substitute for a mathematics course, or why a student had to make a painful choice between Shakespeare and music appreciation. The three divisions cover areas of knowledge that are too large to design meaningful units. I therefore propose a division into seven *academic fields:*

> Mathematics (including statistics and computer sciences)
> Physical science (physics, chemistry, astronomy, geology)
> Life science (biology and psychology)
> History (including such specialties as history of science and economic history)
> Social science (economics, politics, sociology, anthropology)
> Literature (English and foreign, as well as Philosophy, Religion)
> The Arts (music, painting, sculpture, drama)

These fields include all the subjects normally elected for the distributive requirement. They exclude some important subjects; for example, engineering and medicine, which have such heavy prerequisites that they are normally elected only by specialists. We could, however, include some work in engineering in physical science, and some medical knowledge in courses in life science.

Once the seven fields of wisdom are agreed upon, KPW will ask specialists in each of the fields to design one or more three-year units, for students who major in another field, but want a significant experience outside their major. To indicate the type of sequences I have in mind, I shall describe a possible unit in each field.

In mathematics I can speak from personal experience. We have a sequence of six semester courses, all of which are elected by non-specialists with considerable success. Although few students elect the entire three-year unit, this in large part results from the fact that such "specialization" outside one's field is foreign to the current educational philosophy. The first three semesters present an introduction to calculus, probability theory, and vectors and matrices, the major tools in current use by nonphysical scientists. Next there is a semester course in statistics, a course in mathematical models, and a course on computers. I feel that these three years are well within the grasp of any student who can qualify for a good college, and form an excellent survey as well as useful training in the use of mathematics.

A unit in physics presents the difficulty that anything but a watered-down course will require college mathematics. However, one could combine the first half of the previously mentioned mathematics sequence with three semesters of physics as a valuable introduction to physical science. The student who completed this unit could hardly be called a physicist, but his knowledge of physics would exceed that of 98 per cent of the present population.

The unit in life science is very easy to design. A combination of biological and psychological study of man, possibly with some elements of medicine, would be attractive to a majority of the student body.

History departments would find it easy to design a three-year unit either in ancient and medieval, or in modern history. To serve the purpose of KPW, these units should cover much more than historical facts; they should include a history of ideas and of institutions.

The social sciences will need a unit for the scientist and a unit for the humanities student. I shall describe the former, since I have had occasion to give some thought to it. A science student will be attracted by the more theoretical and quantitative aspects of the social sciences. These are only now receiving wide-spread attention, and are usually reserved for the graduate schools, due to the lack of mathematical training of undergraduate social science students and faculty. However, these are precisely the areas that would attract the science student, and might even lead him to a career in the social sciences. The unit should be offered cooperatively by all the departments in the field. The unifying theme should be the attempt to understand groups of human beings by means of scientific (and, if appropriate, quantitative) theories.

I can illustrate the spirit of the units in terms of literature. Rather than survey courses attempting to cover all the history of literature, I would advocate a small amount of survey with a concentration on a significant period. For example, the eighteenth and nineteenth centuries could be chosen for a fascinating unit in literature. The first year might include a semester on "Problems of Philosophy," and a semester survey of the development of ideas and literary styles in the two centuries. Then the student could choose from a variety of courses in philosophy, English literature, and literature in a foreign language of his competence, dealing with the writings of the eighteenth and nineteenth centuries.

In the arts one quickly thinks of a unit on music or a unit on painting and sculpture. I shall, therefore, describe a more unorthodox unit in drama. The unit is designed to study dramatic forms in all major media—theater, movies, and television. During the three years the students would read a great deal of dramatic literature, learn of the techniques of the various media, and acquire "laboratory experience" in the production of pieces. Their reading should be supplemented with the viewing and criticism of plays performed on the campus, of movies, and of TV's video tapes. They should also learn to act, direct, design scenery, make a movie, produce a TV show, and be in charge of the lighting at a play. I know that this unit will raise a number of academic eyebrows, but if it is legitimate liberal education to read Shakespeare inside the classroom, how much more well-rounded will the student be if he learns about all the intricate details of performing the masterpiece!

Let us now look at KPW from the student's point of view. A student is usually required to complete 20 year-courses. These may be divided into semester-courses or quarter-courses, but let us ignore this. The typical student will spend eight years on his major and on prerequisites and cognates. He will be required to take a year of English and a year of a foreign language. He will also have to take two years each in the two divisions, other than the one he majors in, as his distributive requirement. This leaves him six year-courses which he may use either to strengthen his major or to shop around for electives.

KPW hopes to correct two short-comings of the present procedure. It will force students to take high school material in high
school, and will eliminate the fragmentation of the typical curriculum. Given the great desire to get into a good college these days,
there is no excuse for admitting students without a minimum of
reasonable high school preparation. This should include the ability
to read and write English well, competence in a foreign language,
mathematics sufficient to prepare the student for calculus, a reasonable knowledge of American and world history, and a first acquaintance with both physical and life science.

Given this preparation, the required English and foreign language courses should be thought of as "corrective," available for the
occasional poorly prepared student, and should not receive academic
credit. The same should be true of precalculus mathematics, and
the first course in American history. When a student enters college,
he should be ready to take college courses. If he is not, either refuse to take him, or require him to make up deficiencies in addition
to the usual graduation requirements.

Then we are in a position to divide the 20 year-courses as follows:

Eight years in the major, including prerequisites and cognates.
Units of three years each in three fields, other than the field of
    the major; a total of nine years.
Three years for electives.

This program should be adequate preprofessional training in most
subjects. Perhaps the exceptions are engineering, medicine, and
chemistry, with their very heavy prerequisites. For students in these
subjects we could reduce the requirement from three three-year units
to two, but these should be taken outside the sciences.

The three three-year units, added to the knowledge of the major,
will give each student a meaningful experience in four of the seven
academic fields. This represents much more breadth than is normally
achieved today. And, while the student will have a nodding acquaintance with fewer topics, he will have a genuine appreciation
of many more.

Finally, the student is left with three year-courses to deepen his
major, to "waste" on shopping around, or to take that one course
everyone says he must not miss.

Let me finish with a fervent hope that KPW will soon be tried
by a courageous liberal arts college. And, should it turn out to be
my own institution, I sincerely hope that I shall be out of the country when the debate reaches its climax.

As far as the average undergraduate is concerned, the well-qualified science professor is nearly extinct.

The college population is increasing at a fantastic rate. Institutions of higher learning are expanding their facilities, and new campuses are mushrooming all over the country. But many a dean has discovered that it is much easier to build a laboratory than to find a man to teach in it. And if the dean is lucky enough to capture the elusive scientist, he will hardly ever see him in the classroom.

Teaching loads are half of what they used to be. More and more demands are made on the professor from outside his own institution. And, above all, there is the irresistible call of research. Unless the present trend is reversed, the standards of collegiate education in the United States—particularly in the sciences—may reach an all-time low. And the situation will get much worse before it improves.

Not long ago the professor was a scholar, a student of what others were creating, and an able means of passing this knowledge along. Scholarship was at a high point, but research was a rare activity. America relied on Europe for basic research.

The new emphasis on research has slowly allowed America to take a leading position in research throughout the world. The campus of today is a much more exciting place, buzzing with activity. The good student is led to the frontiers of knowledge quickly, and enticed into a creative role. But the price we have paid is a serious decline in the quality of teaching.

There are overwhelming pressures to relieve the ablest men of their teaching duties, and to turn the job over to the less able or less experienced. The university weighs research heavily in promotions. It is much more likely to promote the outstanding creative thinker who is a terrible teacher, than the outstanding teacher who does not do research. After all, the research of the former will bring fame to the institution, while only a handful of students know what goes on inside the classroom.

All the money pouring in from foundations, notably the National Science Foundation, accelerates the trend. It is entirely appropriate to spend government and private funds to strengthen research. But unfortunately the usual side effect is to remove an able man even further from teaching.

Faculty members at an engineering school must devote a significant fraction of their work to sponsored research. Their school badly needs these research funds to support graduate students and to pay for expensive equipment needed to teach modern engineering. If one of the professors wanted to return to full-time teaching, it is not clear whether the institution could afford it.

And colleges are forced to compete with industry for scientists. An aircraft manufacturer with a 100 million dollar government contract can easily outbid the college with its limited funds. It is tragic that Congress refuses to subsidize our colleges, but that it gives vast sums of money to its principal competitors. For example, the computing machine industry could easily absorb every newly trained mathematician for the next 10 years.

We have an image of the college teacher happily spending a lifetime among the protective ivy-covered walls, rarely leaving his castle. Perhaps this was even true at one time. But nowadays it is hard to find a professor who fits this picture. He may be away for a week at a professional meeting. He may be giving a lecture at a sister institution. He may be in Washington helping the government spend its money. Or he may be on a brief trip to Africa, offering friendly advice on how the natives can build their own ivy-covered castles.

There are many professors who spend more time "on the road" than at their own college. Some of this may be in pursuit of additional income (consulting fees are very tempting), but more often than not the trip is an unselfish effort to help someone else, or to further progress in research. It is very easy to argue that the neglect of one's own students for a week is balanced by endless benefit for students at other campuses. But the neglect of students here and now is easier to document than the long-range benefits elsewhere.

The irony of this demand on the time of distinguished professors is that, naturally, the best men at the best institutions are in greatest demand. Therefore, it is the students at the best institutions who are most neglected.

Of all professionals, mathematicians are presently in greatest demand. There are 300 new Ph.D.'s in mathematics each year. Of these more than half go into industrial research. That leaves about one-seventh of a man for each accredited college in the country; that is, if the supply were evenly distributed, the average college could hire a mathematics Ph.D. once every seven years. But the distribution is far from even: all the Ph.D.'s end up at the top 10 per cent of colleges and universities.

Why do these institutions have an insatiable appetite for mathematicians? Partly because their enrollments are increasing. But much more significant is the fact that they get less service from the mathematician each year. The established mathematics professor is likely to be on a research project, to consult, to help edit a journal, to give guest lectures all over the country, to attend at least two professional meetings per year, and to serve on three national committees (one to improve high school education, one to consider the expenditure of Federal funds, and one to see how one could get mathematicians to spend more time on their own campuses). He will take leave every third or fourth year to visit another institution and devote full time to research. He will return home with an offer from the other institution, involving a 20 per cent pay raise and the right not to teach at all unless he feels like it. His own institution either meets the offer or loses a valuable man. And then the college is lucky if the man does not take a second year off, immediately.

There is general agreement that undergraduate instruction in mathematics is poorer than in any other field. And no one seems to know what to do about it.

The sciences give every indication of following in the footsteps of mathematics. A physicist at a good institution will teach one course per semester, and supervise a laboratory taught by graduate assistants. The teaching load in chemistry seems to have dropped about 40 per cent since the end of World War II. And biology is threatened by the competition of the rapidly expanding medical schools. Since medicine has research funds available far in excess of the sciences, a typical teaching load at medical school for an entire year may consist of a dozen lectures plus a five-week laboratory.

The professor's salary is increasing rapidly. And when the pressure of outside offers gets too great, the college will find it more strategic to lower his teaching load as an inducement for staying, rather than give him a salary out of line with others. They may hesitate to add another 10 per cent to his salary, but he will be allowed to teach only three hours a week instead of six hours. The fact that this effectively doubles the cost of his classes is not as immediately obvious as the 10 per cent raise. Nor is it necessarily true.

Very likely two famous professors have their teaching loads cut in half, and someone in a much lower income bracket is hired to pick up the extra six hours of teaching. He may be a graduate student working his way towards an advanced degree, or a high school teacher needing extra income. But most likely it is an instructor on a purely temporary appointment—a man not good enough to share the fame of the department, but good enough to take over half the teaching load of two famous professors. Again, only the students suffer.

Although these pressures are greatest at leading universities, we are now beginning to see the effect of competition on all colleges. A very fine liberal arts college is currently debating whether to give up teaching quality physics, or stay in the market by halving teaching loads—and doubling the staff. A weak institution will fight hard to attract a single name professor, no matter what it costs. An economist at an Ivy League school was offered a position requiring only one course taught per year—just to have his name in the catalogue.

In describing a new position a professor usually comments first on how light his teaching load is. It is a sad fact that the absence of teaching has become a status symbol in the academic world. A man who manages to teach only one course in three years has "arrived."

Just what does the teaching load mean? There is a story of a trustee of a state university who asked a professor how many hours he taught. "Nine" said the professor. The trustee replied: "That's a long day, but at least the work is easy." No doubt the trustee would have been horrified by the nine-hour-a-week load. But the simple fact is that it is a short week, and the work is very hard. Would a professional lecturer like to give nine different lectures in a week? Would the actor like to deliver nine 50-minute soliloquies, and write his own script? Also, the classroom work is only a portion of a professor's duties.

My own institution works on an eight-hour teaching load. Each professor normally carries two courses, meeting four times a week. It may be enlightening to see what a typical week is like, as shown in the chart on p. 108.

As you see, eight hours teaching, plus research, plus all the other activities fill up the week nicely. I am sure that if the teaching load is as high as 12 hours, there is little time for research. And a six-hour week is a significant improvement over an eight-hour week. But beyond that I am not so sure. There is a limit to the amount of time one can spend productively on research. Teaching is a highly satisfying antidote to the strains and frustrations of research.

The few classes taught by a well-known professor are likely to

ANALYSIS OF AN EIGHT-HOUR TEACHING LOAD

	Monday	Tuesday	Wednesday	Thursday	Friday	Saturday
9–10	Prepare Senior Class	Teach Freshman Class	Teach Freshman Class	Prepare Senior Class	Give exam to Freshman Class	Teach Freshman Class
10–11		Coffee	Write letters of recommendation	See book salesman	Argue with Chairman	See student who "can't wait" till office hours
11–12	Teach Senior Class	Office hours	Teach Senior Class	Teach Senior Class	Office hours	Teach Senior Class
12–1	Lunch	Luncheon meeting of faculty committee	Lunch	Lunch	Lunch	Drive to meeting of high school teachers
1–2	Read latest journals			Fill out questionnaires from Dean, Gov't., and two high schools	Correct exam	
2–3			Office hours			
3–4	Short departmental meeting	Find error in research paper	Referee a paper submitted to a research journal	Answer mail		Give lecture
4–5		Try to correct error	Referee a research proposal	Write report for national committee	Visiting lecturer	Discussion
5–6						Dinner
6–7	Dinner	Dinner	Dinner	Dinner	Dinner with visitor	Drive Home
7–8	Work on research paper	Prepare two classes	Proofread previous research paper	Go to movies		
8–9					Prepare two classes	
9–10			Read detective story	Find way of correcting error in research paper!		
10–11	Prepare class					Go to sleep early!
11–12						

be graduate courses. A graduate course is fought for, while undergraduate courses are merely tolerated. To some extent the preference for graduate courses is understandable. In a graduate course the professor discusses his current research, and attempts to interest the most advanced students in choosing the same specialty. If he succeeds, their productivity will in part be credited to him, increasing his own research reputation.

But the overwhelming preference for teaching graduate students is hard to understand. It reminds one of the Wizard of Oz: by handing a senior a diploma, one changes him overnight from an undesirable burden to an attractive asset. One of our visiting lecturers once complained that his institution seems to have few decent graduate students. We later discovered that neither he nor any of his most able colleagues ever teach undergraduates. It did not occur to him that these two facts might be related.

The shortage of experienced professors, and their demand to teach graduate students, lead to an obvious consequence: a large number of elementary courses are taught by graduate students. Sometimes these students are good teachers. But more often, a lack of experience, combined with a lack of dedication, results in a very poor course.

A colleague sent a child to one of the best known universities in the country, only to have five consecutive mathematics courses taught by graduate students. It is hard to see how the very high tuition of the university can be justified if the undergraduate instruction is largely turned over to cheap labor. In effect, the undergraduate student subsidizes the graduate program and the research of the institution. As a result, the student buys prestige from the institution, not an education.

Yet the presence of graduate students can raise academic standards, and future college teachers must acquire experience. A good way of achieving this is the lecture-discussion, or lecture-laboratory course. Lectures are given by an exceptionally able professor, whereas the graduate assistants handle students in small discussion or laboratory sections. It is also desirable to allow *advanced* graduate students to teach a few sections before they graduate. But in each case the work of the graduate student should be under the supervision of an experienced faculty member who can advise him. And every precaution should be taken to assure that no undergraduate gets an overdose of graduate assistants.

In an extreme case, a university introduced lecture sections to use its scarce faculty more efficiently, and then turned some of the lecture sections over to graduate students.

Since graduate students are the preferred clientele, one might suppose that they receive first-class treatment. But even this is not true. We hear of graduate courses being taught in large lecture sections. And thesis-candidates are particularly vulnerable to faculty mobility. I have heard of a Ph.D. candidate who has started his fourth thesis; two of his advisors went on leave, and a third one accepted a position at another institution. Since a Ph.D. thesis is necessarily highly specialized, each thesis advisor asked the student to choose a new topic.

A by-product of all this is the attitude that graduate professors instill in their students. The story of the great man who said "Teaching is easier than digging ditches and leaves more time for research" is well known. Of course he was joking. At least I think he was joking.

Something must be done to improve this picture. We need many more college professors, but that will take time. Some steps could be taken immediately.

Let us examine some sources of the shortage. The National Science Foundation is very generous in awarding postdoctoral fellowships. The effect of these is that the ablest young Ph.D.'s in the sciences do no teaching at all in the two years after completing their graduate training. Since these fellowships carry a great deal of prestige, and since they prohibit teaching (or allow only a minute amount), the new Ph.D. is shown the road to glory. And these men end up at a handful of research centers, leaving most colleges without an adequate staff.

It is easy for the NSF to argue that they have been directed to strengthen research, not teaching. But this is a very short-sighted policy. What is the use of doing more research in this generation when we neglect the preparation of the next generation?

It would be possible to design a plan to strengthen both research and teaching. For example, the NSF could select 100 institutions that combine teaching with research. It could give each a quota of one or more post-doctoral fellows. Each fellow would carry a not-too-heavy load, say six hours per week, and have the rest of the time, plus all summer, for research. The fellows would receive a generous 12-month salary, half from the Foundation and half from the college. That way NSF could support twice the number of fellows, and they would receive experience both in teaching and research. It would also spread the talent over a much larger number of institutions, immeasurably strengthening American higher education.

Such "research instructor" programs exist in various sciences at a small number of institutions, and are very successful. But only the NSF is in a position to make this a nationwide program.

A great deal of scientific manpower is spent advising the government. To assure that federal funds are spent wisely, a panel is called to Washington. For example, to award various summer institutes, 50 scientists take a week off from their universities. Has anyone evaluated the harm done by disrupting 100 classes for a week? I have been generous with my time in helping to evaluate proposals to the government *by mail*. But I have refused to miss classes for this purpose. I urge that in the future all these activities be carried on by mail or by telephone.

But there is a more criminal waste of manpower at most colleges. Since academic institutions are invariably short of funds, they earmark all their money for salaries, buildings, and scholarships, and are very careful not to "squander" their precious funds on other demands. As a result, it is not unusual to find a full professor typing his own letters, copying passages out of books by hand, or writing a long memo where a short phone call would do.

It is still common to find professors taking care of all the boring details of keeping laboratories stocked, and repairing the equipment. The same men, if they decided to work for industry, would have half-a-dozen assistants to make sure that their talents were fully used.

The most extreme case I found was an acting chairman (i.e., a man doing chairman's work without chairman's pay) of a small midwestern department who taught 21 hours a week, corrected homework papers, and did all the correspondence for the department. The difficulty was partly that the department had a vacancy which they couldn't fill. The college was willing to pay the salary of one more professor, if one should turn up by a miracle, but spending a small sum for a secretary, or to pay some seniors to grade homework papers, was out of the question.

This may be extreme, but few departments can handle all the correspondence of their faculty members, provide adequate duplicating facilities, and arrange a pleasant physical surrounding for its permanent faculty. It is even rarer to find an institution enlightened enough to hire an administrative assistant to relieve a department of its endless routine chores.

I have recently heard of an otherwise enlightened institution which has prohibited person-to-person calls from the Campus. This will apparently save the cost of an additional telephone operator. The business office carefully estimated the costs of a larger number of station-to-station calls, and decided that they will come out ahead.

The fact that full professors will spend many extra hours trying to complete long-distance calls does not show up in the budget of the business office.

It seems to me that the only intelligent attitude is to make the supporting facilities proportional to the value of a man's time to the institution. And this value should be measured by how hard it would be to replace him, or to hire another one like him. After all, the supporting facilities save hiring an additional man; and when one notes that faculty in many areas is harder to recruit than are deans . . . but I must stop short of high treason!

Why not offer a new agreement to the faculty? "We know that you want more time for research and scholarship. We will provide this by paying a high enough salary to make outside jobs unnecessary, and by being much more generous with secretaries, phones, duplicating facilities, administrative assistants, and anything else that will save you time. In exchange, you must promise to go back to a reasonable teaching load, and to be around the campus where your students can find you." It would certainly be much cheaper for the college in the long run, and for the faculty it would replace lots of unpleasant chores by somewhat more teaching. Everyone would gain.

It will require a basic change of attitude on the part of administrations. They must face the fact that the college professor has almost vanished, and that the few remaining specimens must be pampered. In exchange, the professor must rededicate himself to his chosen profession.

I would like to propose a 10-point program to improve college teaching. While many of these points are applicable to all fields, they are particularly designed for mathematics and the sciences, the areas in which the shortage is most critical.

1. *Limit the use of graduate students and other cheap labor.* Beginning graduate students should be used only to assist the permanent faculty. Capable advanced students may be used as classroom instructors, sparingly. But if a university has a surplus of graduate students needing teaching experience, it should farm them out to nearby colleges.

2. *Modify the policy on promotions.* Equal weight should be given to teaching and research in the promotion of faculty members.

3. *Use professors more efficiently.* Use them as lecturers where appropriate. Assign assistants to them. Give them all the secretarial

aid and supporting services needed. Relieve them of administrative chores.

4. *Pay generous salaries.* Make the compensation sufficiently large to remove the temptation of consulting.

5. *Return to a reasonable teaching load.* The normal load should be at least six hours per week, with a somewhat heavier load in a predominantly undergraduate institution.

6. *Limit leaves of absence.* Although the traditional sabbatical is unfair, especially to young men, leaves should be taken only after four years of full-time teaching.

7. *Limit out-of-town trips.* The faculty should police itself on this. Is the trip sufficiently important to warrant disruption of courses?

8. *Change the National Science Foundation policy on fellowships.* Postdoctoral fellowships should be available on a half-teaching, half-research basis, with the institution paying half of the cost. These fellowships should be widely distributed. And NSF should subsidize research-time only for faculty members who carry at least six-hours-a-week teaching loads. If the man is allowed to teach less, the institution obviously does not need a subsidy.

9. *Stop calling large groups of scientists to Washington.* A much larger share of the business of advising the federal government could be done by mail or over the phone.

10. *Accelerate the production of college professors.* This is the only real solution in the long run. But it will require extensive reforms in our graduate programs, and the expenditure of vast sums of money. Even then, it will take a generation to return to the teaching standards of another age.

12   THE 3 X 3 SYSTEM

The most important ingredient of a good educational system is a fine faculty. The second most important ingredient is a good student body and the third most important ingredient is a worthwhile curriculum. Generally these are admitted to be the only significant factors determining success in college education.

In 1958, the Dartmouth College faculty undertook a grand experiment to disprove this belief. Keeping the same faculty, student body and curriculum, they decided to adopt a different framework and hoped for improvement of the educational process. The result is the much discussed "three-term three-course" system, or more simply the "3 × 3" system. Under this system the customary semester course is the basic unit, but the calendar is one more commonly associated with a "quarter" system. The academic year is organized into three equal terms and in each term each student elects three courses.

During 1954-55, a committee representing the trustees, administration, and faculty of Dartmouth College considered means of improving education. Taking into account the steady improvement of the quality of entering freshman classes, their primary goal was to further self-reliance and intellectual motivation on the part of the students. The framework of education customary at that time was a two-semester system with students selecting five courses in each semester. It was a frequent complaint that for the average student it was impossible to take each of five courses seriously. It led to a fragmentation of effort in which a student was likely to neglect two of his courses during any given week to be able to carry out required assignments in the other three.

I have vivid recollections of a delegation of students telling me that they had four hour exams in their other courses during the week and could I please excuse them from doing homework for the week. In a sequential subject like mathematics, this destroys the continuity of the course.

It was also argued that a student spending 15 hours a week in class plus additional time in laboratories, and many hours in the various extracurricular activities that are encouraged on the college campus, spends the remainder of his time in required homework and not in the type of intellectual contemplation that should be a prime attraction of a liberal arts college. The committee therefore reached the conclusion that Dartmouth College should follow Harvard's example of requiring only four courses per semester of each student. This would cut down class attendance to 12 hours a week (plus labs) and decrease the fragmentation of intellectual effort. The general framework had been unanimously agreed on; it remained only to spell out details and general guiding principles for the adoption of the new system.

In the fall of 1955, a new member of the committee, representing the science division, was confronted with this action of the committee. Although he was in complete sympathy with the motivation leading up to the recommendation, he felt that the remedy had inherent dangers, particularly acute for science majors. Certainly no one would argue that 40 courses (five courses in each of eight semesters) is a God-given optimum for American college education. However, under the new system the total number of courses would be cut by 20 per cent. When one takes into account that the customary requirements, English, foreign language, and distributive courses, use up about 15 courses, and that in the sciences, prerequisites in the major and requirements of the major are likely to use up 12 more, a 32-course curriculum would leave only five elective courses. This situation would be even more critical for some majors requiring breadth of background material such as engineering, medicine, or chemistry. A typical student in one of these fields would barely be able to fill his distributive and major requirements, and would not be allowed to select a single course purely for the pleasure of it.

The new member of the committee was faced with the dilemma of having to persuade a large and excellent committee to reverse the decision of a whole year's planning. It was clearly impossible to ask them to start from the beginning, his only chance was to come up with a recommendation—on short notice—that would look sufficiently attractive to warrant reconsideration.

A survey of frameworks adopted by major schools indicated that they fell into one of four patterns, 2×5, 2×4, 3×4, or 3×5, with some minor variance on this, such as Princeton's system of having 2×5 for the first two years and 2×4 for the last two years. Of these systems it was clear that the committee's selection of two semesters with four courses per semester did the best job of bringing about the desired concentration. However, this was the system that allowed the least degree of freedom in selecting courses.

It was in this atmosphere that the plan of three terms with three semester courses in each term was first proposed. There was one overwhelming argument against this system: no major college had ever tried this system and, therefore, there must be something drastically wrong with it. However, aside from this consideration, a number of attractive features presented themselves from the very beginning.

If each course met four times a week, this would mean 12 contact hours a week, the same as in the 2 × 4 system. This would encourage students to do more on their own. At the same time, the degree of concentration would presumably be greater if each student had only three courses to worry about in any given term. And yet, over a year a student would complete nine semester courses rather than eight. The total of 36 over the four year period would be a decrease from 40 courses, but only half as drastic as the 32-course system proposed.

It had long been recognized that the so-called "quarter-system calendar" was more attractive than that available for a semester system. The first term would end at Christmas vacation, the second at Easter vacation, and the third term at summer vacation. If the institution wished to adopt a summer term, this would fit in naturally and could be approximately the same length as a normal academic term. Anyone who has ever studied under a semester system, or has taught under it, can remember the frustration of those two weeks in January after Christmas vacation and before final exams. Three weeks' vacation just two weeks before final exams is deadly for the educational process. In many instances these two weeks had to be taken up in trying to recall what was supposed to have been learned before Christmas vacation. For the serious-minded student, the solution was cramming during Christmas vacation, which completely defeated the purpose of a well-earned and psychologically important break in the academic year. The spring semester was better arranged in that Easter vacation came in the middle of it, nevertheless it was not as attractive as the three-term calendar appeared.

The major objection to the quarter calendar has always been the resulting fragmentation of the curriculum. If students took five or even four courses each quarter, making a total of 15 or 12 units during the academic year, then each course became so small a fragment of the total as to lose its significance. Indeed it was hard for the committee to realize that if only three courses were elected in each term, then the quarter calendar could be used to achieve a *higher* degree of concentration than under the semester calendar.

Could a semester course be taught effectively with four meetings a week for ten weeks? It had traditionally been taught in three meetings a week for 14 weeks. Opinions split drastically on this point. The departments of modern languages and mathematics were most enthusiastic about the new system. They were convinced that having students for a shorter period but in a more concentrated attitude was advantageous for the teaching of a sequential subject. Indeed, experience since the adoption of the system has borne out these expectations, and in many cases has far exceeded them. Before the new system went into effect, the language requirement consisted of four semester courses for students who were studying a new language. Today the same is accomplished in three terms, within a single academic year, precisely because the training is concentrated in a single year rather than spread over two years. Indeed, the armed services have accomplished miracles in teaching foreign languages in six weeks in highly concentrated doses. The present system seems to be a reasonable compromise between that, and the overly leisurely pace of the semester system.

Several of the science departments looked forward to the opportunity of teaching three-semester sequences within a single year, in which each course was a prerequisite for the next one. As long as sequences could be of no greater length than two, it has been customary to give two-semester introductions to subjects during the undergraduate years, and put the follow-up course off till graduate school. All of a sudden there was an opportunity to bring at least one graduate-level course into both the junior and senior years by the simple device of scheduling three-term sequences.

Many departments welcomed the greater flexibility allowed by the new system. For example, the geology department requires its junior majors to sign up for three geology courses in the spring term. This enables them to arrange a two-week field trip during the spring term for all junior majors, without having to disrupt the work of the students. Even without this type of departmental organization, students on their own often arrange one term during their undergraduate career when they take only courses in their major. This type of concentrated devotion to a single field gives the student in his undergraduate years an experience similar to graduate work.

Faculty members began to see new opportunities not originally contemplated by the creators of the system. The customary sabbatical system is one in which a faculty member may take a half year off with full pay every seventh year or a full year at half pay. Under the new system it would be possible to take a term off at full pay or two terms at half pay every fifth year. The combination of two terms plus the summer would mean a nine months break from the academic routine every fifth year. Every single young faculty member prefers this to waiting for 12 months every seventh year.

At first the major problem appeared to be the difficulty for departments to arrange schedules which were well balanced over the three terms. Very soon faculty members started to look on this as an advantage rather than a disadvantage. Wouldn't it be more attractive to work harder for two terms and teach only a single course in the third term, allowing ample time for research? In at least one department the schedule was intentionally arranged so as to keep the spring term light, enabling nearly everyone in the department to have a research-concentrated term each year.

The trustee-administration-faculty committee quickly switched its recommendation from the 2×4 system to the 3×3 system, and hastened to bring the recommendations to the general faculty. (The word "hasten" in academic life means that it took them only a year to bring the matter to the faculty.) But no system could be as good as this system sounded at the time. The faculty opposition during this period amounted to a fever pitch.

The opposition took a variety of interesting forms. For example, there was the professor of botany who pointed out that ten weeks is not long enough for a plant to grow to full maturity, therefore the teaching of botany would become impossible. There were experienced lecturers who felt that cutting the term from 42 classes to 40 classes would make it impossible for them to present the required material. And there were the professors giving large lecture courses who feared a decrease in their enrollments if a student had to elect their course from one out of three instead of one out of five courses. And, above all, there were the large number of faculty members who argued that the new system would present the faculty with a much heavier load.

Under the semester system the average faculty member taught three courses each semester requiring a total of nine classes per week. They thus taught six courses each year. The committee proposed that the simplest equivalent teaching load would be that a man should again teach six courses per year, which under the new system would mean two courses in each term. Since each course met four times a week, this would in effect mean a reduction of the teaching load from nine hours per week to eight hours per week. It was the hope of the committee that the time the faculty thus saved could be devoted to the supervision of independent work on the part of students.

Be it recorded to the credit of the distinguished faculty that they were not going to be fooled by correct arithmetic. Anyone could see that under the old system they were teaching nine hours in each of two semesters and hence had an 18-hour teaching load per year. Under the new system, they would teach eight hours in each of three terms, and hence would teach 24 hours per year, leading to a one-third increase in the teaching load. Woe onto the tricky committee that was trying to get away with imposing one-third more teaching on the faculty under false pretenses!

While this was the commonest computation, I had the pleasure of seeing at least six other arguments ranging anywhere from showing that the new system would cut down the teaching load by 50 per cent, to arguments that under the new system the faculty would be required to teach 100 per cent more.

Of course, there were various legitimate objections to the new proposal. It remained to be shown that students can really absorb certain types of materials in 10 weeks. It was pointed out that final exams would come three times a year rather than only twice. Although the total number of final exams any one faculty member had to administer would be the same as under the previous system, it is more cumbersome to have to worry about them three times in the year.

In this case the registrar of the college made a major contribution. He pointed out that if a student takes only three courses, the problem of cramming for finals should be slight, so that the standard 10-day final exam period could be reduced to 4½ days. As a result of this, the traumatic experience of final exams has been minimized. A student finds it much more feasible to cram for three final exams at a time than to try to keep all the material in five different courses in his mind.

It was legitimately pointed out that if courses meet four times a week they cannot be given on alternate days. Thus in one way the weekly calendar will be less attractive than under the previous system. However, this disadvantage was balanced by another ingenious scheme of the registrar. He worked out a weekly timetable in which five hours are reserved for each four-hour course. The special "X hour" was reserved for the course for a variety of purposes. For example, it could be used to give an hour exam. It could be used to make up an hour in case a faculty member was ill. And, most usefully, it could be used to move a class to this period in case the faculty member has an out-of-town commitment. This has led to a serious reduction in the number of times the faculty member has to ask his colleagues to substitute for him, and hence has provided much more continuity for each course.

These and many other arguments were brought up on both sides of the issue. The faculty with its usual majestic pace argued in a dozen faculty meetings over two academic years. I personally favored the change to the new system, but I must admit that if eloquence alone could win an argument, the opposition should certainly have carried the day. When all the smoke cleared the issue seemed to be fairly well delineated: the new system apparently promised major improvements over the old. However, it was a new system, and as yet untried. It meant change, and it meant that faculty members who for three decades had taught under one system would have to learn new tricks. When the final secret ballot was taken no one was prepared to predict the outcome. The final vote was exactly two to one in favor of change.

The success of the system has exceeded the fondest hopes of its creators. The vast majority of the faculty and student body is enthusiastic about the new system. The students are working harder, they appear to be more serious, the library is used much more heavily, and there is a marked change in the academic atmosphere. The enthusiasts are still enthusiastic, men moderately in favor of the system have acquired enthusiasm, and the strongest opponents have been silent.

A survey after three years has indicated that the best students far prefer the new system, the average students like it at least as well, only the weakest students on the campus are opposed to the new framework, for the simple reason that they have to work harder. The college has been swamped with inquiries from sister institutions who want to know what the strange new system is about.

No one claims that the new system is perfect, we are still trying to improve it. But the college has demonstrated that any intelligent attempt to improve upon tradition even in so unimportant a matter as the framework for education, can be significant. Ivy-covered institutions are traditionally the defenders of tradition. It is comforting to note that on rare occasions these bastions of all that is good in our legacy from previous generations can also be the source of what is radically new.

PART III COMPUTERS

13 MACHINES AS EXTENSIONS OF HUMAN BRAINS *

Man's most remarkable characteristic is his ability to overcome his natural limitations. Much of human history is the story of Man overcoming his physical limitations. Guns, bulldozers, cars, airplanes, and mass-production plants are all means by which Man extended his brawn. The computer revolution promises to do as much for extending Man's brain.

It is important to realize the validity of this analogy. Anything done by a bulldozer could instead be done by a large enough group of humans working sufficiently long. But the task could be so unpleasant that it would never be undertaken without a bulldozer. The increase in the speed of travel has vastly changed our way of life, even though all the trips now possible by car or plane were possible previously. The difference is between a trip of a few comfortable hours and the hardships of many months.

There is nothing that a high-speed computer can do that humans couldn't do without the computer. Nevertheless, computers will revolutionize our life because we will now undertake tasks we would never have dreamed of in the past.

What can computers do? Any task for which we can give precise instructions can be programmed for a computer; and the computer will do it much faster and with a negligible chance of error. Let us illustrate this in terms of numerical calculations. If we take as a basic task an addition ("take a number A, add to it a number B, and write down the answer as C"), we find that the machine Dartmouth College has on order will perform 2 million such operations per minute. For a human being, equipped with an electric desk-calculator, the same task would take three years. And if we let the computer work for 24 hours, it would accomplish a task that would take 100 human beings their entire lives. And there is an excel-

---

* Based on a commencement address given at Woodstock (Vt.) Country School, June, 1960.

lent chance that the computer will not make a single mistake in 24 hours, whereas 100 human beings during their entire lives . . .

The giant electronic brains now make practical tasks which we have known how to do—in principle—before, but which were out of the question previously. We have already made great use of computers in physics and engineering, in tracking astronauts and in predicting the weather. But the eventual impact of computers will go far beyond computational applications. My purpose in this essay is to discuss five potential uses of computers to nonnumerical problems. Each one of these is just over the horizon. And together they paint a picture of how electronic brains will change our lives during the next generation.

Let us first consider an application to medicine. There is a doctor for every thousand people in the United States. If he is a typical doctor, he is a general practitioner, who has been out of medical school for many years, and has had little chance to keep up with the hundreds of medical journals reporting the fantastic progress in medicine. Most of the cases he diagnoses are routine. But once in a while he is not sure. He needs expert help. He would like to call in a specialist. But this is expensive, timeconsuming, and may be impractical in a small town. And he may not even know what kind of an expert to call.

The next generation of doctors will have a central computer available for consultation. We must get together the leading diagnosticians of the country with a number of computer experts. The diagnosticians must be asked to describe just how they make a diagnosis. This is harder than making a diagnosis, since—in effect—they are asked to tell how they act under all possible circumstances. Over a period of years the computer programmers will translate this information into a gigantic diagnostic method for a large computer.

Then the general practitioner can call up the computer and tell it a list of symptoms observed in a patient. Very likely, the symptoms will not identify a unique disease. So the computer will ask for further information. For example, the G. P. may be asked to perform a certain test on the patient's blood. After the requested information is furnished to the computer, the machine identifies the ailment, and describes the recommended treatment. If it is a serious case, it may recommend calling in a specialist.

It is important to observe that all the key decisions are made by human beings. The local doctor examines the patient, and the method of diagnosis is due to recognized specialists. But the computer makes the collective effort of specialists available, all over the country, on a moment's notice.

Next I shall pick one of many possible examples in which a computer is used as a planning device, in which nature is imitated.* My example is the control of traffic in a large city, say in Manhattan. There is an endless effort in progress to improve the flow of traffic through this congested island, but while a 10 per cent improvement is made, the number of cars increases 20 per cent, and the bottlenecks get worse every year.

How does the city try to correct the problem? They collect vast amounts of information about traffic conditions and about the causes of bottlenecks. Then they make some adjustments. For example, they make a street one-way, or they change the length of time that a light is red, or they prohibit parking on one side of a street, etc. But after a series of changes they must wait a month or more to evaluate the effect, before they can make further changes.

Basically their procedure is sound. But why not do it on a high speed computer rather than use us poor drivers as guinea pigs? One can build a model of the traffic pattern of Manhattan in the memory of a high speed computer. This would contain a street map, information on traffic regulations and on lights, the rate of traffic flow, and the type of traffic encountered. It could also contain some probabilities, such as the frequency of taxis pulling out of lanes, the likelihood of a truck blocking the street, or the probability of an accident.

Then the computer could run through a typical day's traffic, including all the problems that arise, in a few minutes. In an hour it could repeat this often enough to spot the major trouble-spots. Then it could automatically make adjustments. *It* makes streets one-way, or changes lights, or bars trucks from a given street, all inside its memory. Then it spends another hour testing the new pattern. In six months it would come up with improvements far better than anything the traffic commissioners could possibly have dreamed up and at a fraction of the cost of the present experimentation.

My third example is from the field of law. There is one task facing lawyers that is essentially routine, time-consuming, and unpleasant: The search for precedents. Therefore, it is an ideal task for a computer. Some very interesting experiments have already been run along these lines.

Suppose that a case involves the liability of a school for an accident occurring on its property after school hours. One can key the machine to search for "liability" and "accident" and "school property" and "after hours," or synonyms of these, occurring all in the same case. A well-designed program will turn up all conceivably relevant cases,

* See Essay 14.

and probably many irrelevant ones. But picking out the relevant ones is a much smaller task once the machine has narrowed the search to a small fraction of the original volume.

Actually, the bottleneck in this case is not in computer programming, but in the input devices. Once all the court cases in New York State are on tapes, the rest is fairly straight-forward. But today we are forced to type these endless volumes onto cards and transfer them to tapes—a time-consuming and very costly procedure. This problem, and many other "information retrieval" problems are waiting for the development of an efficient photoelectric scanner that will transcribe the printed page directly onto magnetic tape. We can expect such a device within the next decade.

Much has been written about the importance of computers for scientific work. But most of the impact so far has been in data-handling or in the computation of examples. What can the pure mathematician or theoretical scientist hope to gain from computers? Of course, he too is interested in examples. But most of his work deals with formulas.

I have participated in one of the many attempts that have been made to use present-day computers for formula-handling. My impression from these experiments is that while computers are clearly capable of handling formulas, they are not very good at it. Considering the vast advantage computers have over humans in numerical work, it is disappointing to find how slight an advantage the fastest computers have over us in handling symbolic work. Apparently we have found certain short-cuts which are either not possible on computers, or—more likely—which we are unable to explain to computers.

One of two things must happen before computers become as important for theoretical work as for numerical computations: either new design will arise, yielding computers better suited for symbolic work, or we must have a major breakthrough in the way present computers are programmed for symbolic work. When either of these developments becomes a reality, the electronic brain will revolutionize pure mathematics and theoretical physics the way it has already revolutionized engineering and business.

I saved for the last, the development whose long-range effects are beyond my abilities at crystal-ball gazing. This is the possibility of computers learning from their own experience. If we can explain to a computer, no matter how crudely, how we learn from experience, it can acquire the experiences of a hundred lifetimes within a single day.

This idea has already been utilized to teach a computer how to play good checkers or chess. At first the computer learns how to play a crude game, learning all the rules, and making simple-minded decisions. In other words, it plays like a novice. But then it is told that on the basis of success or failure it should adjust its method of decision. Then two computers are left alone for 24 hours, playing an endless number of games against each other. At the end of the day each is playing an expert game.

In any game there are certain factors on the basis of which the status quo is evaluated. These may be the number of pieces, their values, and their positions. The computer calculates all possibilities two or three moves in advance, evaluates each, and decides which one will be best (assuming an intelligent opponent). It can then try to improve its chances of winning by increasing the importance of certain factors and decreasing others, testing the results on a large number of games.

While this technique has been developed for games, it is applicable for most decision-making situations. One always calculates various possibilities, and evaluates the likelihood of success. And we continually learn from experience. Why not use the high speed computer to acquire the experience of a thousand lifetimes for us?

Man has excelled by overcoming his own limitations. His major shortcoming has been that he has had to learn from his own mistakes. Perhaps in the future the electronic brains can explore all possible mistakes for us, and we can profit from their experience.

14 GAMES OF LIFE AND DEATH *

Science began when Man decided to observe Nature systematically and to discover the laws of her behavior. For many centuries this meant that Man had to go to Nature and be a passive observer of her activities. But eventually Man decided to bring Nature indoors, where he could observe her at his own convenience. Thus was the first laboratory created.

At first the purpose of a laboratory was to reproduce some phenomenon of Nature exactly as it occurred normally. This was usually expensive and extremely slow. So the scientist turned to models which, he had reason to believe, would imitate the original. He isolated simple features of Nature. He reproduced large-scale phenomena on small scale, and very small-scale phenomena on reasonably large scale. He replaced mechanical systems by electric-circuit analogues, and electric circuits by mechanical analogues. The possibilities along this line are limitless, and most laboratories will for some time continue to be of the *analogue* kind. However, this procedure requires new equipment for each new and different type of problem.

Today, large electronic computers provide a lazy man's dream laboratory. He does not have to go into the wide world and strain his eyes or get his hands dirty observing nature. He does not have to construct laboratory equipment patiently and painfully, and he does not even have to follow the path of a mathematical theoretician. He simply buys a giant brain for a few million dollars, or persuades his employer or government to provide one, and he is ready to experiment in far-reaching fields for science, industry or government.

The key to success here is *simulation.* The computing machine is told in general terms how a certain phenomenon takes place in nature, and then it is programmed to run through this type of activity a few million times under varying circumstances, to observe itself and to give a simple summary of what has happened. We hope that soon we will also be able to program the giant brain to formulate

* Reprinted, by permission, from the January 21, 1963, issue of *Nation*.

hypotheses, to test them and to inform us of the best theory fitting all the circumstances. The day cannot be too far off when leading scientific journals will accept papers written by giant brains of the nonhuman kind.

The easiest way to explain simulation is by example. A group at Dartmouth College was interested in whether there is any basis in baseball for the way a manager arranges his batting order. The data here is very simple. We are given a team of nine men (an ex-Brooklyn fan had selected the 1952 National League Champion Dodgers for the purpose). We informed the machine of each player's batting percentage, as well as the frequency with which he gets walks, extra base hits and home runs, and how likely he is to hit into a double-play. We then asked the machine to arrange the batters in a certain order and play through the 154 games of a regular season, computing how many runs the team scores in a typical season. We then tried other batting orders, looking for the best one.

The results* showed definitely that batting line-ups are important. The difference between the best and worst batting order can average one run per five games—quite enough, over a year, to make the difference between winning and losing a pennant. In this instance, the best batting order was found to be the one that was actually used in the World Series. Small differences in line-ups, the computer showed, are not nearly as significant as some managers seem to feel. The batting order has to be changed drastically before a statistically significant change in run-making power occurs.

Of course, none of this comes as a surprise to an experienced manager. However, we reached our conclusions via a computing machine—not a particularly large one, either—in a day's computation; it takes a manager many years of experience to acquire these bits of baseball lore. Herein lies the advantage of simulation.

In one of the re-created seasons, we kept a careful record of individual performances. Hodges hit 40 home runs, Robinson led with a batting average of .344, Campanella hit three home runs in one game and Furillo had five hits in another. In one game, all nine players hit safely; another was a one-hitter pitched against the Dodgers. In one fabulous game the Brooklyns scored 19 runs! In short, it was a quite typical Dodger season.

Many of the numbers corresponded very closely to those of the 1952 season. For example, the team batted .260, as compared with .262 in reality; and they hit 152 home runs on the machine, while

* The hard work was done by George Cooke, then a sophomore research assistant at the Dartmouth Computation Center.

hitting 153 in reality. Other statistics varied more—as they would from season to season.

It is particularly interesting to note hitting streaks and slumps. Cox had a seventeen-game hitting streak. When this happens in an actual season, commentators describe the batter as being in a "hot streak." Such a streak can be accounted for by statistical fluctuations; other, longer ones, such as Joe DiMaggio's famous streak, must have involved some psychological elements. It is worth noting, in this connection, that the longest hitting slump recorded by our computer was a six-game slump by Campanella. Longer slumps, quite common in baseball, probably also involve psychological factors.

Is there any value in electronic simulation if we are unable to reproduce psychological factors? At the very least, the technique helps us to determine what effects may be ascribed to psychological rather than statistical causes. Moreover, we are able to make allowance for some psychological factors, once we understand them. For example, if we know that a certain batter is in a batting slump, we can easily program the machine to reduce the probability of a hit. Or again, if the player is a good clutch-hitter, we can tell the machine to increase his probabilities of hitting whenever there is a man on base. The more our programmer knows about baseball, the more realistic a baseball game he can construct.

The two major uses of Man's new laboratory are for planning and for training. We used it at Dartmouth as a planning device, to determine the ideal batting order for a given team. However, one can visualize a school for baseball managers in which the machine plays full nine-inning games between two opposing teams, indicating on a screen what happens at each stage. The opposing managers could interfere at any point, changing pitchers, sending in pinch hitters, putting on hit-and-run signs, etc. They could acquire a whole season's managerial experience in about a week, and at the same time receive an impartial evaluation of how good they are as managers.

How can a simulated baseball game resemble a real game, when no two real games are ever exactly alike? The answer is that no two games simulated by the machine are exactly alike, either. Electronic computers are perfectly capable of simulating statistical procedures in which it is not determined how a given batter performs at a given moment; the machine is guided simply by the laws of probability and by the player's known batting average. When the batter's turn comes up, the machine generates what is technically known as a "random number"; the size of this number determines the outcome. If a given batter has a 30 per cent chance of hitting, a 10 per cent chance of getting a walk and a 60 per cent chance of being out, then the machine generates a random between 0 and 10. If the number is between 0 and 3, the batter is awarded a hit; if it is between 3 and 4, he walks; if it is between 4 and 10, he is out. The technique reproduces the statistical features of the game with remarkable realism.

A major use of the simulation laboratory in recent years has been the training of businessmen. Experts in a certain area of business, for example in the stock market, program a computing machine to simulate the behavior of the market. When the budding young tycoons assemble around the machine, they buy and sell stocks; they may play through a five-year business cycle in a single day. The machine produces the price fluctuations, and in the end some of the players will be rich, some will be broke—and all will be wiser for the experience. Of course there are dangers that the designers of the training model will build their own prejudices into the situation. However, the impact of five years of experience in a single day, even if the model is far from perfect, is incomparably more valuable than the tedium of having to read the financial page daily for some 1500 days.

Similar procedures are applicable to the scheduling of production in a large company. The same model can be used equally well for planning purposes, and has been so employed by large industries. The chances are that a group of computer experts can, by trial and error and the application of some mathematical ingenuity, arrive at a production plan far better than one devised by the most experienced collection of vice presidents. This does not mean that experience will be useless in the age of automation; it does mean that experience combined with the use of giant electronic brains will be more useful than experience combined with the miniature natural brains most of us have available.

Planning bodies have not yet awakened to the possibilities of planning by simulation. For example, the way traffic lights are controlled in a large city is a haphazard affair. The mathematical problems involved in "optimizing" the setting of lights are beyond our present capabilities, and are certainly not solved by the people who usually plan these matters. It would seem economical and efficient to expedite things by the use of giant brains. Let the traffic commissioner's favorite plan be programmed on a computing machine, let several thousand programmed cars loose in the city, and let us see how long it takes them on the average to reach their destination. Then let us try other programs, making minor adjustments here and there, until the flow of traffic is improved 100 per cent. This is not too different from present-day planning, which is also by trial and error, except that actual cars with actual drivers are used over periods of years. Switching to the simulated laboratory would speed up planning at less cost to drivers' nerves.

The most interesting, and perhaps most frightening, use of Man's newest laboratory is in the so-called "war games." A group of military and civilian experts feed to the computing machine the best available data on the military capabilities of two opposing countries. Let us say these countries are the United States and Switzerland (one must be careful not to violate security regulations). Opposing general staffs lay out careful battle plans, and then a war is carried out. The machine traces the path of each major military unit, decides the results of combats by random devices (e.g., a plane of type A has probability 75 per cent of destroying a plane of type B), and then carries the surviving units on to the next battle, according to the general staff's plans. At the end of the game the results are announced in terms of how many millions of people were killed on each side, and what fraction of the military potential of each nation was destroyed.

Of course, the same war has to be played through many times according to the same strategic plans, since chance variations may make the difference between victory and defeat. Thus the conclusion may be that the United States wins this war (the victory probability may turn out to be 68 per cent) at an average cost of 41 million lives. Then the opposing general staffs can try to improve the battle plans with the aim of increasing their probabilities of winning and decreasing their losses.

Most people's first reaction to this use of computing machines is one of revulsion. But this attitude, human enough, is also naive. If a major war should come, it will certainly mean the loss of tens of millions of lives to each side. Without doubt, the enemy has excellent computing machines of its own, and should it decide to attack, it will have planned its strategy with great ruthlessness and efficiency. The United States has decided that the best deterrent to war is to be thoroughly prepared for reprisal. In the age of atomic warfare thorough preparation means more than simply the availability of a great deal of war material. The stupidity of commanding generals has cost countries all over the world tens of thousands of lives in battles throughout history. In the next war, the inefficiency of a commanding general might cost millions.

Modern war has become too complex to be entrusted to the intuition of even the most experienced military commander. Only our giant brains can calculate all the possibilities. As long as the world is insane enough to contemplate a nuclear war, the war had better be well planned. Perhaps the best way to avoid war is to make sure that, every time our opponent simulates the war on his computer, the answer shows that the United States has the overwhelming probability of winning.

A different type of activity, also known as a war game, has long been used for the training of military leaders. Simulated battles are actually carried out in various types of maneuvers, giving commanders experience in the field. These maneuvers are expensive, both in money and in time, and at best they give a military commander a single "war" experience in any given year.

Simulation laboratories should become required equipment for all officers' training schools. Prospective commanders should have varied experience in directing battles under circumstances far more realistic than those afforded by field maneuvers. They could acquire the experience of a hundred major wars before graduating from OCS. This type of laboratory work would seem to be much more valuable in the age of nuclear warfare than the marching drills now required of ROTC students.

I have a further suggestion. One of the major deterrents to agreement on complete disarmament is national pride and a long tradition of belief in the glory of war. Neither need be given up even if all destructive armaments are turned over to international control. Let us agree to continue to produce armaments of the most destructive kind—on paper.

All of this information can then be fed to great simulation laboratories at the United Nations. Whenever the international scene gets too tense, let one side "attack" the other, notifying the Security Council of what attack plan it is using. The defending side, duly informed, must immediately submit its plans of defense. The great war is played out on the largest and most expensive computing machine ever constructed by man. After 24 hours of computation, both sides are informed of the outcome. The victor can then rejoice, and the defeated country—after paying due reparations—can start arming for the next simulated war.

Surely the permanent substitution of simulated war for actual war would be the supreme achievement of Man's newest laboratory.

15 A LIBRARY FOR 2000 A.D.*

THE NEED

Since I am about to propose a radical reorganization of university libraries, I must first establish that some such reorganization is inevitable. I shall argue that our university libraries will be obsolete by 2000 A.D.

Harvard University will have a library of more than 10 million volumes by 2000 A.D. Dartmouth College will purchase its one-millionth library volume during the bicentennial celebrations of the college, in 1969–1970, and if the present rate of growth continues, the second million volumes will be purchased in 35 years. At that rate of growth, universities will have a full-time occupation in the twenty-first century building new libraries.

It is clear that the cost of building, of purchasing volumes, of cataloguing, and of servicing these monstrous libraries will ruin our richest universities. Even if Harvard University conceived a 10-million volume collection as physically feasible, this would only postpone the decision by a few decades, since the collection of 100 million volumes that one could predict for 2100 A.D. could not possibly be handled in a manner similar to the procedures of any existing libraries.

As our present libraries grow in size they also become increasingly difficult to use. Library catalogues are growing into giants and are approached with fear by both students and faculty. Unless one knows the exact name of an author (including initials) or unless one knows the exact title of a book, it may become hopeless to locate it. And once a mistake is made, it is best to forget about it and start all over again. For example, many libraries have discovered that if a book is misplaced on the shelves and cannot be located after a short search, it is less costly to replace it than to try to find it.

That the very conception of the way books are made available is wrong can best be illustrated in terms of an actual example of a

* Part of the MIT centennial lecture series, 1961. Reprinted, by permission, from *Management and the Computer of the Future*, edited by Martin Greenberger, MIT Press, Massachusetts Institute of Technology, Cambridge, Mass.

search I recently carried out in the Dartmouth library. Table 1, below, will give a factual account of the search.

TABLE 1. AN EXAMPLE OF SEARCH

Walk from 328 Dartmouth to Baker Library	4 min
Find card in catalogue	30 sec
Walk up four flights	1 min 30 sec
Find that book is missing	15 sec
Walk down four flights	1 min
Find out that Prof. S checked out book	30 sec
Walk from Baker Library to 329 Dartmouth	5 min
Wait for Prof. S to return from lunch	2 hr
Wait for Prof. S to find book	15 min
Total search time	2 hr 27 min 45 sec

As one can see, there are two major bottlenecks in the search procedure. First of all the physical running around is a very significant proportion of the time I spent in using the library. Dartmouth College's library is fully open stack; if it were not, then someone else would do a great deal of this running around, and the time consumed would be considerably longer. But even the actual catalogue look-up and the running-around time together is negligible compared to the delay caused by the fact that once a book is removed from the library it is likely to be out of circulation for at least two weeks. If Professor S borrows a book, he is likely to have it on his shelf anywhere from one week to one year, during which period he might use it for a total of less than one hour. Of course, one could require him to use the book only in the library; but if he wishes to consult it a dozen times during the coming weeks, it is most unreasonable that he should have to spend a considerable amount of time on each occurrence in locating the book. It is clear to me that as long as libraries function in the present manner this problem is unsolvable.

I have saved for last the most acute problem of search today. How can a worker in field X find out in a reasonable amount of time what results are known concerning problem Y? For example, there are several hundred mathematics research journals published in the world, and in addition to these, hundreds of volumes of mathematics books appear each year. Relevant information for a research problem may be contained in the numbers of any one of 50 journals spreading back over the last 30 years, or in any one of a hundred books. To find half a dozen relevant items, it may be necessary to search thousands, and the odds are great that some crucial piece of information will be over-looked.

This problem is so critical that it must be solved and solved relatively rapidly, independently of the problem of the reorganization of libraries. (This is, of course, the problem of the retrieval of scientific information.) However this problem is made more acute by the clumsiness of our libraries. If, to search through 200 books and journals we have to locate each one by the procedure sketched above, and may have to wait until 20 of them are returned to the library by colleagues, the problem becomes completely hopeless.

In summary, our libraries are practically obsolete today. They are certain to be obsolete by the end of the twenty-first century, and will for most purposes be useless by 2000 A.D. It is therefore appropriate to consider a radical reorganization of the entire scheme of university libraries, and it is by no means too early to begin planning today.

STATEMENT OF THE PROBLEM

If my proposals are to have serious scientific merit rather than turn into science fiction, I must impose certain restrictions on the solutions of the problem. First of all, I shall require that my library be within the capability of our technology by 2000 A.D., and I shall require that it still be useful at the end of the twenty-first century. More than that one cannot possibly hope for. No one can foresee the needs of the year 2100 A.D. nor the tremendously powerful tools mankind will have available by that time. Specifically this will mean that the only devices that may be used are those that will be available within the next two or three decades, and that the library should start with some 10 million volumes and have the means of expanding by a factor of 30. (At the present rate of growth, one would expect a growth by the factor of eight within a century. I am allowing a factor of 30 since I am certain that the rate of expansion will increase. If the rate should turn out to be much more rapid even than that, then the library about to be described may become obsolete before 2100 A.D.)

Secondly, the library must solve the present bottleneck in making items available to research workers. The time to take out a book from the library should be of the order of magnitude of a few minutes at most.

Thirdly, there must be a reasonable procedure for finding out where information is available. This procedure should be applicable not only to search by author or by title, but to search by subject matter.

Finally, I want to put realistic financial restrictions on my library. A solution in which the cost of purchasing, cataloguing, storing, and making information available increased the library budget of every university by a factor of 100 is not acceptable.

BASIC PRINCIPLES

If one accepts the statement of the problem in the previous section, there are a few basic principles that are easily arrived at. For example, it is clear that the library of the future will have to make heavy use of automation. There is no conceivable way in a library of several tens of millions of volumes that human effort could locate an item in a matter of minutes. I will, therefore, proceed on the assumption that I can make free use of whatever machinery can be designed in the near future, even if this will drastically alter our conception of a library. However, I will try not to propose the use of a machine where a human being can perform the same task more efficiently. Just as the majority of mankind resists the introduction of automation, owing to very natural but irrational prejudices, the minority of mankind that is pioneering automation has the tendency to use machines in place of human beings whether this can be justified or not.

It is equally clear that while the physical format of books is very convenient for human handling, it is most inconvenient for machine processing. A simple calculation of the volume occupied by 100 million books shows that even if they were solidly packed, without room for humans to move around in, they would occupy a building of impressive size. If we were to have reasonable access to the books, we would presumably need a building greater than the Empire State Building. Therefore, storage methods must miniaturize books and put them on a medium easily handled by machines, for example, some type of tape.

The very crudest estimates for a feasible library will put the cost of construction somewhere in the 100 million dollar to billion dollar range. It is not reasonable to expect that individual universities should spend sums of money of this order of magnitude. Indeed, it is difficult to see even today how one can justify the tremendous waste of effort in which each university has its own staff to order books, to classify, and catalogue them, and run a variety of duplicative reference services. I will therefore adopt as a basic principle that we are designing a single central library that will serve for research purposes both the federal government and the major universities of the country. I shall refer to it as the *National Research Library*.

In such a centralized library many functions will be no more costly for the entire country than the cost at any individual institution. Even where the central library will have to allow for a considerable amount of duplication, presumably the merging of 100 university libraries will not need more than ten times the expense of an individual library. Therefore I estimate that the actual cost of a central library might be of the order of magnitude of 2 or 3 per cent of the cost of building 100 individual libraries.

I will further assume that it will take our universities some 20 years to decide that their libraries are rapidly becoming obsolete. This will leave them an additional two decades to complete the National Library by 2000 A.D. If each of 100 major universities agrees to contribute $100,000 per year from 1980 A.D. to 2000 A.D., and if the federal government matches these funds, we would have 0.4 billion dollars available for the construction. Since many of the universities will actually save a good deal more than $100,000 per year, and since the federal government could easily contribute a larger sum of money, it is perhaps reasonable to allow up to 1 billion dollars for the planning, design, and construction of the National Research Library.

It may be appropriate to say a few words concerning the likely fate of present libraries in the twenty-first century. I will take it for granted that our university libraries will *not* be abolished, even if their role becomes secondary. Partly this will be due to the fact that they will serve a limited but useful purpose, but mainly to the fact that faculty members will be reluctant to give up personal contact with books.

Aside from purely sentimental reasons for maintaining our libraries one can certainly make a strong case for keeping on a given campus any book that may be consulted as often as once a week. This would certainly include the present reference rooms, as well as core research libraries in all subjects. The periodical room would still serve as useful a purpose as in the past, though perhaps it would be wasteful to preserve most of the periodicals. The students would have books on reserve, though they should also be encouraged to use the National Research Library, so that they become familiar with its operation. One must also take into account that our university libraries play a major role in leisure time reading, and the pleasure of browsing should not be taken away from either students or faculty.

All of these functions can be fulfilled comfortably with a collection of no more than a few hundred thousand volumes. I estimate this number generously, since I feel that the sentimental attachment of faculty members to books is very strong. Our present libraries could be decimated in 2000 A.D., to cut them down to such a reasonable working size. The number of volumes could then either be kept constant by removing less often used books and replacing them by current ones, or a very slow rate of growth could be permitted. In either case a considerable amount of room would be freed under this scheme, and could be used for faculty studies and reading rooms (which are now in great demand and in short supply on most campuses). One would also want to put aside part of the library as reading rooms, in the new sense described in the next section.

ORGANIZATION OF NATIONAL RESEARCH LIBRARY

We are planning a library which will start with some 10 million volumes and which may grow to 300 million volumes during the twenty-first century. I will propose a basic division of the material in this library into *subjects*, and a division of the subjects into *branches*. The fundamental unit of storage, search, and retrieval will be known as an *item*.

A rough examination of the Dewey Decimal System which, although out of date, still is basically sound, suggests that present day knowledge may be classified into 100 major categories that I will call "subjects." Roughly speaking, a subject corresponds to the first two digits in the Dewey Decimal System, or in a modernized version of the same; for example, mathematics, identified by the digits 55. Allowing for the increased complexity of knowledge in the twenty-first century, I will assume that the number of subjects will be doubled during the lifetime of the library. I think that this is a realistic assumption; certainly the number of subjects must grow at a much slower rate than the number of volumes.

Each subject will function as a unit in the new library, and will have its own room and complete means of storage, search, and retrieval. The National Research Library might originally consist of 100 large rooms, and might have to grow into a structure of 200 rooms. This is a much more modest rate of growth than any library can foresee in the immediate future.

From now on I shall discuss only a single subject, since each subject will be organized on the same basic principles as each of the other (roughly) 100 subjects. As my standard example I shall use pure mathematics; a rough estimate would show that pure mathematics and applied mathematics are each of just about the right size to be represented as 1/100 of a research library. According to the estimates in Table 2, a subject should grow by some 6×10^4 items per year in 2000 A.D. A subject that would reach that rate in 40 years should today grow at some 25,000 items annually, which would make pure mathematics a possible small subject. However, it would indicate that chemistry will have to be treated as five different subjects in 2000 A.D.

A subject will be divided into a number of "branches." The basic restriction on this division will be that most problems be classifiable as falling within a single branch. I have used as my guide in this matter the journal *Mathematical Reviews,* which publishes brief descriptions of everything that appears in print in mathematics. From the journal's subject index, it is reasonable to estimate that by 2000 A.D. pure mathematics may be divided into 50 branches. I will allow the number of branches of a given subject to grow up to 100. At this stage it would appear better to have the subject subdivided into two subjects.

As an estimate of the size, growth, and complexity of the central library we may take the figures in Table 2. These figures are guesses at averages, which should be fairly reliable at least to their orders of magnitude.

TABLE 2. SIZE OF LIBRARY

	2000 A.D.	2100 A.D.
Volumes	10^7	3×10^8
Items	3×10^8	10^{10}
Subjects	100	200
Items per subject	3×10^6	5×10^7
Items per subject in a year	6×10^4	10^6
Branches	5×10^3	15×10^3
Volumes per branch (with duplicates)	4×10^3	4×10^4
Items per branch	10^5	10^6

Within a given branch, material may be classified into books, and books may be subdivided into "items." By an item, I shall mean roughly a chapter of a book, or an article in a journal. By definition an item will be somewhere between one and 50 printed pages, and I would assume that most items would be 10 to 30 pages in length.

If publications continue in anything like their present form, this would seem to be the smallest reasonable unit for storage and retrieval.

At this point I should like to propose a basic modification of the manner in which items are stored. I can illustrate this in terms of a research journal in mathematics. A given volume of a research journal is likely to contain articles on a wide variety of topics in mathematics, and only a small fraction of these would be of interest to any one research worker. It would be much more sensible to collect all articles that are published in a given month which relate to a given branch, and label them as a "volume." Since items will be stored by branches, some such procedure will be essential. Of course there will be the difficulty that some articles will be relevant to several different branches, and in this case we should bind copies of the same item into several different volumes, and add them to the library of all of these branches. Thus a volume will be a homogeneous collection of articles relating to a single branch. The classification of items according to branches will of course be crucial to the success of our National Library. However, this does not seem to be an unsolvable problem. For example, in mathematics, where the American Mathematical Society operates *Mathematical Reviews*, each reviewer is even now asked to suggest a classification or classifications for the article he reviews. Similarly, our library could retain experts in all fields, to write abstracts and to indicate to which branch or branches the article most appropriately belongs.

Each item could be catalogued by a code name consisting of three letters and nine digits. For example, in the code ABC-12-34567-89, the letters ABC designate the subject and the numbers 12 the branch. The volume within the branch is indicated by 34567 and the item within the volume by the last two digits. By consulting Table 2 we can see that this reasonably simple coding system could take care of the needs of the twenty-first century. If one visualizes retrieval of information by means of a device similar to a telephone dial, we find that we have available roughly 5×10^{11} combinations, whereas our maximum need is for some 10^{10} labels. This degree of "waste" is certainly necessary if the coding system is to be at all natural.

For example, an expert in probability theory would soon learn to dial MAT-17 to obtain access to his specialty, after which he could dial a seven digit number to obtain a specific item.

THE PROBLEM OF STORAGE

We must now face up to the problem of storing several hundred thousand items, belonging to a given branch, on a single tape. There is every reason to believe that within the next hundred years miniaturization will make it possible to store all the volumes in the library in a small box. However, our devices must be available in this century, and they must make items available quickly and inexpensively. Therefore a page should be reduced only to a size from which it can be magnified to its normal dimensions optically. This would indicate that we should store each page on a millimeter square. This degree of miniaturization is essentially feasible today, and will certainly be practical in another two decades.

We are now in a position to store all the articles of a given branch on a tape with roughly the dimensions 2 in. by several hundred ft. Let us refer to a 1 mm cross section of the tape as a "line." We will store all the pages of a given item on a line. (We should note that a 2 in. width is exactly right to allow the storage of up to 50 pages on a single line.) Since the basic unit of storage and retrieval will be an item, it will be convenient to have copying operations done a line at a time.

If we estimate that a branch will have a maximum of 10^6 items, we must allow tapes of 3300 ft lengths. Since current high speed tapes may be 2400 ft long, the manipulation of library tapes could be handled by a device not very different from tape units now employed.

How long would it take to retrieve a given item from such a tape? The current devices can run through the entire tape, filling in or copying every bit of it, in five to 10 minutes. Of course this speed can easily be improved. And we must take into account that we would rarely want to copy any significant portion of the tape; we may instead employ a rapid search device to find the beginning of a volume, and then copy the relevant items from the volume at a more modest speed. We may therefore safely assume that we can build tape devices which, given the code numbers of some 20 items in half a dozen different volumes, could copy the items onto another tape in less than one minute.

I therefore visualize the room as having some 100 tape units for the storage of books concerned with the given subject. Typically the subject would have 50 different branches and therefore without duplication 50 tapes would suffice. Indeed, some branches would be consulted sufficiently rarely that a single copy of its tape will make material quickly accessible, but in the more popular branches two or three duplicates of the same tape will be desirable. If we assume that each customer ties down a tape unit for one or two minutes (and we will see that this is a safe assumption), then we may estimate the number of duplicate tapes necessary by requiring that during the busy part of the day no more than 30 to 60 customers per copy should wish to consult the tape. Even in a central library it is safe to assume that a device that can satisfy some two hundred customers per day will suffice for many branches. And it is hard to think of branches in which more than two or three duplicate copies will be required.

Since storage will certainly be one of the major expenditures in any future library, it is worth pausing to estimate the cost of storage. In 2000 A.D., we shall have to allow approximately 10,000 tape units. Since they will be produced in such great numbers, the cost per unit should not exceed a few thousand dollars, making the expenditure for storage less than 100 million dollars—entirely within the range of our budget. This estimate indicates that the 1 billion dollar figure given earlier for the total cost of the library is a very generous one, but it does show that the total cost will have to run to a few hundred million dollars. During the century the number of tape units may quadruple. This would mean an annual expenditure of between one and two million dollars, which will be a reasonable fraction of the total operating cost of a library that serves the entire country.

One of the advantages of storing items by branches will be the ease with which new items can be added. Since the numbering of volumes of a given tape is arbitrary, one may simply append new volumes at the end of the tape, assigning the next available serial number. I would propose that although the National Research Library should operate night and day, every day, each subject should be "closed down" one day a month for the addition of new material and for necessary checking and repairs. The addition of some 100 volumes to a branch should be a very simple operation. The material could be put on a master tape during the rest of the month and transcribed onto the appropriate branch tapes on the special date. If the mathematicians of the country get used to the fact that the mathematics library is closed on the 13th of each month, this will be of very little inconvenience to them in the long run.

It will be an important safety device to keep one copy of each branch tape in a vault, to be available for the repair or replacement of parts of the tape that become damaged or "worn out." Or it may in the long run prove simpler and cheaper to replace each tape at the end of the year by a copy from the master tape. From here on I will ignore this problem of the updating of materials and the question of repairs, since there is no essential difficulty in either.

RETRIEVAL OF INFORMATION

Let us now turn our attention to the user of the National Library. He will be located at his own academic institution, and therefore the institution must be connected to the central library by means of a multichannel cable on which pictures can be transmitted. Such devices have already been developed, and we can expect them to be in general use soon. The university will have a large number of reading units scattered around the campus, some at the university library, some in departmental reading rooms, and some in individual professors' offices. The number of these units and the number of channels to the central library will no doubt depend on the size of the institution and on its "library budget."

The reading unit may appear similar to a microfilm reader, but it must be equipped with a tape unit capable of receiving pictures from the central library, each picture representing one page. The unit must also be equipped with some means of sending signals to the central processing unit; for the sake of simplicity I shall picture this device as a telephone dial.

The customer turns his set on, and begins by dialing the three-letter code of the subject of interest, say MAT for pure mathematics. This connects his reading unit to the central processing unit for pure mathematics, and makes a projection unit available to him at the National Library. Next the customer dials the two-digit code number for a branch (say 17 for probability theory) or for a catalogue (say 00 for author catalogue), or a special code for some other service provided by the central library.

For example, the customer might dial MAT-00-ART. This would connect him with the mathematics rooms, and with the author catalogue in that room. He would start looking through the author catalogue with authors whose names start with the letters "ART" and he could "flip through" the catalogue by pushing a button on his set which instructs the projector to advance by a page.

The idea of having library catalogues arranged by subjects is so simple and practical that it is hard for me to believe that it is not now in general use. Surely it would speed the finding of a given book, if, instead of having one gigantic catalogue, one would have it divided into a hundred segments corresponding to individual subjects. In most cases the customer would immediately find the correct subject; and even in the worst case he is unlikely to have to look in more than two or three subjects. Having to look in card files one one-hundredth the total size would, I am certain, speed up the retrieval procedure considerably. Except for this modification in the arrangement of the catalogues, the author and title catalogues—which are among the more efficient features of present libraries—would not be drastically different from present files.

Once he finds the listing of the item he desires, he can dial its nine-digit code number to obtain the item itself. A slightly different code could be used if he wishes to obtain an entire book (e.g., using 00 in place of the item number). With a little skill and some thought it should take a customer less than 5 minutes from the time he turns on his set to the time that he has retrieved an item of interest from storage.

This makes it very convenient for the user who obtains an item, but what about his many colleagues who would like to look up the same item while he is perusing it? Of course we would no longer have items tied down for several weeks, only for the period that the item is actually being read; but in a library servicing 100 universities this would still be an intolerable bottleneck. Fortunately there is a simple way to handle this problem: the customer is never allowed to use an item directly from the files, but only a copy of it.

When an item is requested, this is transferred from the storage tape to the projection unit, by copying one line, and from there it is sent—conveniently magnified—to the tape in the reading unit. The latter tape might be visualized as similar to a 3-minute length of video tape. Such a tape can receive information at a speed of an item a second even without improving on today's technology, and it can hold about 10 volumes.[*] Once the items wanted are copied onto the reading tape, the customer "hangs up" and frees the storage tape and projection unit for his next user. He can then read the transcribed items at leisure. Once he has finished with these, he may either keep the tape for his personal library (a 10-volume collection of personally selected items on a 10-dollar tape!) or reuse the tape next time.

As previously indicated, dialing MAT connects the reader with the Mathematics Room, and procures a projector. Next, dialing 17 connects the probability storage tape unit to the projector. As he dials the five digits of a given volume, the storage unit carries out a high-speed search, and the final two digits of code instruct it to

---

[*] Assuming that we store one page per exposure at normal camera speed.

transfer an item (or an entire volume) to the projector. While the next item is being dialed by the customer, the projection unit transmits the previous one to the reader's tape. Thus items may be obtained just as rapidly as the customer can dial seven-digit code numbers. The average customer should not tie down the storage unit for more than a minute or two. This procedure will also hold the cost of long-distance consultations to a minimum.

A similar procedure could also be used in looking up items in a catalogue. Instead of tying down the catalogue while the customer searches, relevant portions of the catalogue could be copied onto his reading tape, and he could search the catalogue at his leisure.

The reading unit could be of a relatively simple type. It would have to hold a short tape on which it can receive pictures at normal

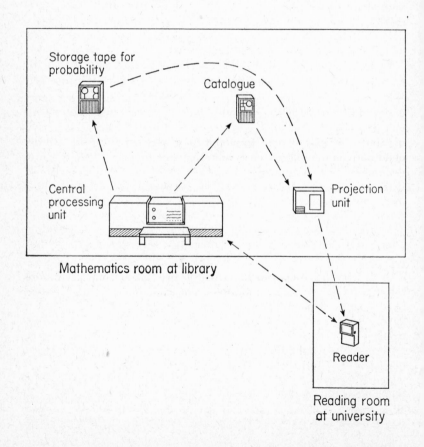

camera speed. It would present this tape a frame at a time, magnifying it as in an ordinary microfilm reader. It would have to be able to advance the tape a square, or move back a square, and to move to the next item, or to back up to the previous item. In addition to this, the unit would have a signalling device—say a phone dial—for communicating with the central library. It is reasonable to expect that such units could be mass-produced at a cost that would not only allow each institution to purchase a number of these, but that even individual professors might obtain private readers.

Each reading unit would be furnished with a "telephone book" containing the code names of subjects and the code numbers of the branches of each subject. To make use of this book practical, under each branch there should be a brief description of the contents of this branch, since—as we will see later—correct identification of branches will be crucial for search purposes. As the complexity of the library grows, the division into subjects and branches will have to be revised every 10 years, and thus new "telephone books" will be issued at the beginning of every decade.

Any number of additional uses of this set-up suggest themselves. For example, we have already noted the possibility of a customer recording interesting items for his personal library. For a particularly important item it may be desirable to have a copy available in normal size, and thus we may wish to attach a photocopier to the reading unit. The exact extent to which these services are used will depend both on the relative costs of permanent copies vs. long-distance calls, and on the frequency with which the items are needed. Unless they are used very frequently by the customer, it must be recalled that it will take him less time to obtain a new copy from the central library than to find the item in question in his personal library.

Or again, we could attach a projector to the reading device, which shows a page on a screen. Not only would this make it easier for men with visual defects to consult the library, but it would enable the mathematician to lie down on his couch while he thumbs through the latest research journals. The same device could be used in a seminar or a research conference, allowing all participants to have simultaneous access to an item from the National Research Library.

I want to emphasize that I have devised these ideas during a period of a few months, and I am forced to consider subjects in which I am not an expert. However, I believe that even this crude sketch establishes the fact that a storage and retrieval system to meet all of my conditions *can* be designed by 2000 A.D. I am quite certain that a group of 100 experts in a variety of fields, cooperating over a period of 20 years, could come up with a scheme for a central library that will be as far superior to my proposals as my proposals are to our present obsolete libraries.

For example, one of my Dartmouth colleagues suggests that instead of having the National Research Library centralized, it could be located at various major libraries, each serving as the custodian for one or more subjects. Although such decentralization may be more costly to maintain, it might have many advantages. If each major library had a complete projection unit available, the local library could have on tape frequently used copies of items from all subjects, and all the catalogues, thus cutting down significantly on the demands on long-distance cables. Of course a user need not know the actual location of a subject. His request would be taken care of automatically by the usual means for routing long-distance phone calls. Thus, the alternate scheme amounts to a decentralized but unified National Research Library.

This leaves us with but one major problem, namely the problem of searching for information relevant to given scientific problems.

THE PROBLEM OF SEARCH

Let us consider the problem of finding information relevant to a research problem in a typical branch in the middle of the twenty-first century. Hopefully we manage to pinpoint the problem as belonging to a single branch. This still leaves us several hundred thousand items to search. It is in this area that the high speed computing machine could make a significant contribution. So far we have automated our library to a considerable degree, but we have employed only machines of the simplest possible type. Only the problem of search is sufficiently complex to justify the use of a "giant brain."

Let us make our problem more precise. It is entirely reasonable to expect that for search purposes we have available a relatively brief abstract of each item in the branch. For example this could be a coded version of a review in *Mathematical Reviews*. Of greater use, a general scheme for the format of *Mathematical Reviews* could be agreed upon by the American Mathematical Society, and reviewers could be asked to write their reviews in this specific format. At any rate, each item is represented by one coded page, and we are to search relevant pages among several hundred thousand. Let us first consider two extreme solutions of the problem: in one, the machine will play a role that is trivial, and in the other the machine will play an exceedingly complex role.

The simplest role the machine could play is that of a gigantic memory with a simple tree-like pattern built into it. Experts in a given branch are asked to subdivide the branch into subbranches and divide those into topics and those into subtopics, etc., making at each point some 2 to 10 subdivisions until the partition is fine enough that any one cell has a sufficiently small number of items in it, and that the research worker could reasonably be expected to examine all the abstracts in the cell. If we start with say 5×10^5 abstracts and wish to narrow it down to 20 abstracts in a typical problem, there must be 25,000 subdivisions of the branch. This would put a tremendous strain on the experts who are to arrive at the classification scheme, and the probability of taking the wrong fork in the search processes would almost necessarily be very high. Nevertheless this is a possible scheme and therefore I have carried out a small experiment to see how well it could work.

I took the 200-odd articles in pure probability theory that were reviewed in one year in *Mathematical Reviews*. Starting with the division into 10 subbranches of that journal, I introduced a division into topics, and in some cases into subtopics. If the system worked well, it narrowed the abstract down to two or three after only two or three questions. I must confess that I had great misgivings about this system even while I was designing it, since in some cases papers could legitimately belong to several categories, while in others it was hard to find common features for any significant number of articles.

The results of the experiment were catastrophic. In 13 search problems, performed by three probabilists—with an assistant of mine playing the role of the machine—the abstract was located on the first try in five cases, after a small number of tries in two more instances, and not at all in six cases. It was not uncommon that the very first division, that taken from *Mathematical Reviews*, lead the searcher into the wrong category. I have since learned that reviewers for *Mathematical Reviews* frequently refuse to classify papers more accurately than into branches, because of the ambiguity of the other divisions. I therefore conclude that this method of search cannot be practical on a large scale.

At the other extreme the entire burden could be placed on the computer. The customer could furnish it with information as to what type of problem he is considering, and the computer would be asked to search through the hundreds of thousands of abstracts to try to detect ones that appear to it to be relevant. It would then present the customer with all these abstracts, and the customer could choose amongst them. I feel quite certain that a scheme similar to this will be entirely practical 100 years from now, but rough estimates seem to show to me that in the immediate future such a procedure is still utopian, and that if the scheme is not to make too many mistakes and yet be successful in narrowing down the abstracts to a couple of dozen, the computational time involved would be prohibitive.

I therefore come to the conclusion that a scheme that is to be practical in 2000 A.D. and stay practical for a few decades would have to be some sort of give-and-take between the human being and the high speed computer. Although the complete classification scheme I described seems to be too cumbersome a system, a partial classification would certainly be practical. *Mathematical Reviews* divides each branch into something like 10 subbranches. My experiment indicates that this is not completely safe in that even at this stage of division the chances are great that the customer will be in doubt as to which of two or three branches he is interested in. However I can conceive of a series of 10 questions in each branch that the computing machine might ask the customer, and the research worker could indicate in each of the categories all those topics which might possibly be relevant to his search. It would be important to allow in each case the option of indicating that the particular method of division is irrelevant to the problem in question. I would visualize the give-and-take as follows: the machine flashes to the reading unit a list of alternatives, and the customer signals back by dialing the relevant numbers. Perhaps an answer of zero could indicate that the method of subdivision is not helpful. If even half of the questions turn out to be relevant, and in each case the possibilities are cut in third, you will have narrowed the number of abstracts down to about 2000.

At this stage the computer would be called upon to perform a more essential role. It would search these 2000 abstracts and try to find features that many of them share. It could then ask the customer to indicate which of these features would be of interest to him. The computer could also indicate after each reply how many abstracts are still "in the running." After three or four exchanges of information the list of abstracts should have decreased to a manageable quantity.

This would appear to be a more fruitful division of labor. The experts in the branch would be asked to devise 10 criteria on which items may be classified, and the reviewers would have to indicate for each criterion how the item should be classified. This is a practical procedure as long as it is not expected that in the cross partitioning every combination (or even most combinations) should occur, nor that the final output of such classification needs to be a very small number of abstracts.

It is crucial that in the search the customer be allowed to declare that a given method of classification is irrelevant. For example, one obvious criterion might be the date of publication. For some purposes only the last ten years need to be considered, which would narrow the search considerably, but for a question of priority the date is irrelevant. Again for some other purposes the last 30 years would suffice. Thus the experts might suggest listing the last 80 years in 10 year intervals as 8 categories, and "older" as ninth, with "irrelevant" being the tenth. Then one researcher might narrow it to a single category, another to one of three categories, while still another would ask that this criterion be ignored.

The searcher would have ample opportunity for using his skill, in trying to narrow the search, without loss of valuable information. It could also be left to his discretion as to when he decides that the search has narrowed sufficiently for his purposes. For example, if he is trying to compile a bibliography, he is likely to want to look at a much larger number of abstracts than if he simply wants to know whether a certain theorem is known to be true.

Finally, the machine plays a significant role, but on a practical scale. Clearly the ingenuity with which it is programmed to classify the remaining abstracts into "similar" ones will make all the difference in the speed and likelihood of success of the operation. Yet we are not asking of it anything that is beyond the likely developments of the next 20 years, nor anything that would take more than a few minutes per stage.

In summary, each component seems to be playing a near optimal role: the experts in the field can suggest useful questions that will in most cases narrow the field; the customer can use these criteria optimally for his own purpose, and can make the final selection from a short list of abstracts; whereas the computer serves partly as a memory for questions, and partly as a rapid device for the rough classification of a large number of abstracts.

I would propose that the search-machine be also programmed to observe its own operations and to improve its procedure as it learns from experience.

An incidental benefit of the compromise solution is that it does not require extra hardware at the customer's end. His reading device and dialing system will be sufficient. He can dial a suitable code, and then simply answer questions presented to him on his screen by dialing all relevant numbers. Finally, when the search has narrowed sufficiently for his taste, he would signal the computer to put all the remaining abstracts on his reading tape, and he could examine them at his leisure, noting down call numbers of relevant items.

To test these ideas, I carried out a second search-experiment.* Taking the probability publications of one year as my data, I designed a scheme by which each item was to be classified as to whether it had present in it one of 50 interesting features, falling into several major categories. The searcher was to indicate all features of interest to him, and our Dartmouth LGP-30 was to find all items having these features. In the experiment the coding was carried out by my assistant, who was not an expert in probability theory— which no doubt had a serious effect on the outcome. Then each subject was asked to pick an item from the year's product, and to list its significant characteristics (from the list of 50), judging from an abstract of the article.

Strictly speaking, this experiment was no more successful than its predecessor. It produced about 50 per cent success in some 30 tries. However, whereas the first experiment seemed to be hopeless, the second one had several promising features. For example, when it succeeded, it was too successful: it often produced only one or two abstracts. This seems to indicate that a cruder classification would have sufficed. When it failed, it usually failed because the searcher noted some one feature that the classifier did not include. In many cases this was directly due to the inexperience of the classifier, and my assistant feels that if the classification had been performed by an expert, the percentage of success would have been much greater.

It is also significant to note that failure usually resulted in no abstract being turned up at all. In many cases a repeated search, omitting one criterion at a time, produced the desired abstract, without producing too many others. Thus, there seems to be every hope that an improved search scheme along these lines would be reasonably successful.

But there are also a number of danger signals present in the outcome. It is most disturbing to note how easy it is for two experts in a given field to disagree whether to include or exclude a significant feature. I am now convinced that any search scheme in which one "wrong" answer dooms us to failure cannot possibly work. It was also significant that the subjects were invariably eager to ask

---

* In both experiments I was ably assisted by George Cooke, then a sophomore research assistant at Dartmouth.

the experimenter additional questions. I do not see how some "conversation" with the machine can be avoided.

A second disturbing feature is the length of time necessary for even a simple search. Our method required about $\frac{1}{2}$ minute per item. Of course, on a faster machine this can be cut by a factor of 10^3, and in the future it is likely to be cut by an additional factor of 10. But there is reason to believe that as the number of items increases by a factor of n (and the number of criteria by a factor of perhaps $\sqrt{n}$), the length of search time may increase by a factor of n^2. Since we expect a branch to have some 1000 times as many items as the number we searched, this could mean an increase of $10^6/10^4$, or by a factor of 100. And search times of the order of an hour are prohibitive.

It would be easy to answer that this will no doubt be improved upon with the progress of technology, but we have already admitted that the techniques I tried were too primitive, and that slower techniques will have to be used. Thus here is one area where considerable improvement in computer design and use may be required. Of course this research will be of vast value for many other purposes, and we may expect this research to take place whether or not we decide to build a National Research Library.

This still leaves the question of what type of machine is required for search. Should it be one gigantic machine for the entire National Library, or one for each subject? If the latter is not prohibitively expensive, it would certainly be preferable. But here I would estimate that 200 machines with the capabilities desired would exceed our budget. I, therefore, suggest a single gigantic computer as more practical. The computer could operate on a single master program, with tapes giving it the suggested questions for any one branch and having on file all the abstracts of the branch.

The machine should certainly be designed so that several customers can consult it simultaneously. This will eliminate some of the waste resulting from the fact that the customer thinks at a much slower rate than the machine. Recent developments in computer design would indicate that there should be no difficulty in having 100 or even 1000 simultaneous consultations.

If this turns out to be practical, a customer could dial INF to be put in touch with the information-search machine, and then dial the code for the subject and branch. From then on the procedure would be as indicated before.

Of all the problems discussed in this paper this is the one requiring most study. I expect that it is an area where a group of experts could make vast improvements on the scheme I have proposed.

CONCLUSION

I have argued that our present libraries will be obsolete by 2000 A.D., and that the library of the twenty-first century must be designed on entirely different principles. I hope that I have answered this challenge by describing a possible library for 2000 A.D. within the reach of technological development, and within a realistic budget.

I find the concept of such a library very attractive. I am basically a lazy person. I should like to sit in my office and have access to a book with no more trouble than calling a friend on the phone long-distance. Of course, I may occasionally get a busy signal, but few of us would argue that this makes the phone impractical. I have tried to argue that we would get busy-signals less often than the frequency with which the book we are looking for is out of our library today. And we could arrange our calling system so that we can hold on and obtain access to a storage tape as soon as one is freed for the particular branch—which should be within minutes.

I am particularly attracted to the prospect of combining this automated library with machine-search. I would hope that this feature alone would justify the great central library. It is possible that, even with all this elaborate mechanization, information retrieval will become hopeless in 100 years—but without mechanization we won't have a ghost of a chance. I look forward with delight to being able to find everything relevant that has been written on a given subject in 10 minutes—or finding out that nothing relevant has been written.

I do not claim that this will save money for our universities in the long run, but I do believe that only in this way will they be able to continue operating at anything like their present library budgets. The alternative is either to abandon any degree of completeness, or to increase library expenditures to fantastic sums.

And we must realize that the incidental benefits of change will be tremendous. Most important, of course, will be that all participating universities will have access to all the books of the National Research Library. The impact of this single fact on research could be so great that all my estimates for growth could prove too conservative.

But we can also visualize an endless list of auxiliary services, tied to the central library. For example, a search service could be established for the convenience of industries needing quick and thorough information on past research in a given field. When one considers the hundreds of organizations now offering partial services along this line, it is not inconceivable that this service alone could bring in enough income to finance the National Research Library.

But I am more interested in the variety of new services that could be made available to university staffs. It is a research worker's dream to think of a system that would provide all the items published in his branch during the past month as the result of a single call. All it would take is a special marker at the head of the items added during the past month. Then one could dial a special code, say MAT-17-99999, to obtain a transcript of all these items. Or alternatively, one could be furnished with abstracts of all such items. It is the only way that I can conceive of mathematicians keeping up with their specialty in 2000 A.D. And think of the needless duplication resulting from lag of information that would be eliminated!

Again, it is reasonable to assume that machine translation will be available by 2000 A.D., hence the reader should have the option of obtaining an item in the original language or in translation.

Equally promising is a scheme for compiling a bibliography for a research project. The potential user would furnish a list of relevant articles, and a brief description of the project. The central machine would then look up the bibliography of each article, check them for relevance, and look up the bibliographies of the new relevant items, etc. This procedure, a familiar one to research workers, would condense weeks of work into minutes. Even if it produces a number of irrelevant items, it would be very valuable for research purposes.

And, no doubt, the reader will think of some pet projects of his own that will become possible in a National Research Library.

It is also safe to predict that the effect of such a library on the very nature of research will be immense. I don't dare to explore this subject too far, for fear of sounding fantastic, but I do want to raise one possibility. Isn't it conceivable that the nature of publications will change? Why should we continue to publish hundreds of journals in each subject, when the simple act of depositing an item in the National Library would accomplish more? We could visualize a time when research results in mathematics are simply submitted to the "mathematics editorial board" at the National Library, where they would receive the customary referees' treatment. Once accepted, they are filed into the National Collection, together with an abstract of the accepted format, on the next 13th of a month. Any library or individual would then have access to the item, and could obtain a copy of it by the procedure described earlier. The time of "publication" could be cut to about three months from the present two years, and the cost would return to normal proportions.

My purpose has not been to say the last word on this subject. After all I have suggested 20 years duration and an expenditure of one billion dollars for the design and building of the Library. I have only tried to show that even after so brief a period of thought one can design something vastly superior to our present libraries, and hence I hope to have established the possibility of a National Research Library for the twenty-first century. My fondest desire is that others should go far beyond my modest beginnings, and that someone may be persuaded—sometime during the next two decades—to do something about this vital problem.

16 COMPUTING CENTER AT A LIBERAL ARTS COLLEGE *

Many colleges and universities do a fine job in training a small number of experts in the use of high speed computing machines. Dartmouth College itself turns out a dozen or more of these in each class, who compare favorably with the best computer programmers in the country. However, this is not the main challenge facing the liberal arts institution.

The advent of high speed computers may bring about a revolution comparable to the Industrial Revolution. The lives of all of us will be significantly affected by the existence of these artificial brains. In addition to the small number of people who will personally use these machines, millions will be indirectly affected by their very existence. It is essential that a student receiving liberal arts education should, in the future, be acquainted with the potential and limitations of high speed computers.

Since many students at an institution like Dartmouth become executives or key policy makers in industry and government, it is a certainty that they will have at their command high speed computing equipment. If they are aware of possible uses of these machines they will be able to carry out their future tasks much more efficiently. If they share with the older generation the basic fears of man-machine relationship, the chances are that the head of their computing department will, in effect, give orders to them. In short, liberal arts training in use of high speed computers is essential to make sure that in the man-machine relation, man is the master.

Dartmouth College shares with other leading educational institutions the fact that its faculty combines teaching and research. Many projects nowadays can make use of high speed computers to facilitate research greatly. However, it is important to note that, with a few exceptions, these problems are of a medium rather than a large size as far as today's high speed computers are concerned. (See the classification of problems that follows.)

There is a general tendency to measure research needs in terms

* Presented to the Trustees of Dartmouth College, April, 1963.

of the actual machine time required to solve the problem. However, in all small and medium size problems, and even in many large problems, the most significant time is not that of the actual running of the program. Before a complicated research problem can be run on a computing machine, a complex program must be written and tested, or as the technical jargon goes, "debugged." It is a common experience among research workers that debugging takes many hours of their time, and indeed, is the greatest single factor to discourage faculty members from the use of high speed computers.

Although any computing center on the campus will have to meet the vast majority of needs of faculty members, there are two considerations that must be kept in mind. First of all, any reasonably high-speed machine will take care of 99 per cent of the research needs of faculty members on the campus. For these problems, convenience in debugging is more important than the actual time it takes for the problem to run. Second, extremely long problems usually take a very long time to debug. Hence, spreading out the computing time over several days, or even sending the problem to another center, is tolerable.

It will be convenient to classify problems roughly into three categories:

1. *Small problems.* We may define these as problems requiring only a few thousand steps to solve, and the computing time required ranges from a fraction of a second to a few seconds. Into this category would fall most uses of the high speed center for educational purposes as well as most debugging runs on research problems.

2. *Medium problems.* These are problems that require a few million steps to solve, and the computer time is of the order of magnitude of a few minutes. The vast majority of research problems would fall into this category.

3. *Large problems.* Problems that will stretch any high speed computer to the limits of its capacity will require the order of magnitude of one billion steps. These will use up several hours of computing time. Such problems will be rare and will require weeks of preparation. Therefore, receiving answers to these within a few days is entirely satisfactory. It is expected that large problems will be run overnight.

Using this classification, we can state that in an education-research combination, one would expect 90 per cent of the problems to be small, 9 per cent to be medium size, and 1 per cent to be large. Plans for a computation center must be made relative to these facts of life.

It is our conviction that where most computing centers err is in designing the entire center for the most efficient operation of large problems. This is a significant consideration from the machine usage point of view, but not from the point of view of most users, who will never write a large problem. In general, our plan will differ from that of conventional centers as follows: at the conventional center the designers usually maximize the time that the machine is in use. We are interested in minimizing the time it takes for a given user to receive an answer. These two differing goals lead to entirely different modes of operation for the computing center.

On small and medium size problems the time to get the problem into the machine and out of the machine may be longer, even significantly longer, than the actual running time of the problem. For example, a typical student problem or a typical debugging run on a large-scale research problem is unlikely to take more than 5 or 10 seconds of computing time. However, it is not possible to get this problem into the machine and out of it again in less than a few minutes' time.

This difficulty is dramatized by a recent experience at one of our sister institutions. They trained a group of mathematics students during a two week "reading period" in the rudiments of using a high speed computer. Each student had to write two simple programs and try them out on the machine. Naturally, beginning students made many mistakes and had to use the machine repeatedly. With only 200 students trying to solve two problems each, this project managed to tie down for two weeks one of the fastest computers in the world. The irony of the situation was that the computer itself was standing idle 99 per cent of the time; however, the problem of getting the students on the machine and off the machine, and giving them several chances to correct their problems, completely tied up the input and output devices.

What are the customary solutions to this problem? The commonest solution is to collect a large number of small and medium sized problems and put them all on a magnetic tape. This tape is then read into the machine and the machine works on one problem at a time, writing the answer on another magnetic tape. When the entire cycle is completed the answers are printed. This is extremely efficient from the point of view of machine usage, but about the most inefficient operation from the point of view of getting an answer to the human customer. Even if the actual computing time on the machine is 1/1000 second, the human customer will have to wait several hours to obtain the results of the computation.

To make up for this well known difficulty, computing centers compromise in allowing a few minutes two or three times a day for special debugging sessions. This certainly serves to improve the situation, but the result is still far from ideal. It is not at all uncommon for experts at some of the largest computing centers in the country to require several weeks to debug serious research problems. During these weeks they will have to come to the machine, at the machine's convenience, and adjust a great deal of their time to the needs of the computing machine.

Whatever solution we are going to adopt, we will certainly not allow the computing machine to dictate schedules for faculty and students. Instead, we wish to design a system where the machine is there for one purpose only, namely, to serve human beings.

THE PROPOSED SOLUTION

If it takes much longer to get a small problem into the machine than to service it, and if we are determined to give fast service to students and faculty, then it is clear that problems must be inputted into the machine simultaneously. Our proposed solution is to have the problems inputted immediately through one of some 20 simultaneous input devices, and then have the problems wait in line in memory until the time comes up for servicing. It may at first appear that there is no significant difference between having the problems wait in line inside the machine or having the customers wait in line outside the machine. However, there is all the difference in the world.

Since it takes, typically, a few minutes to type out the problem and feed it into memory, students waiting in line outside the machine may have to wait until a dozen other problems are inputted and outputted—a matter of an hour or more. However, if the problems are inputted simultaneously and the student only has to wait until each of a dozen small problems is serviced by the machine, and each service may require only a few seconds, or even less than a second, it is quite likely that the student will receive an answer to his own problem within a minute or two. The reduction of the waiting time from hours to minutes could make the difference between a successful or completely frustrating educational experience.

To enable operation of the type described, it is essential that in addition to the main machine (the central processor), there be a secondary machine acting as a buffering and switching device. This buffer receives simultaneous inputs from a number of typewriters, lines up the characters, sorts them out, does simple editing, and has them ready for the central processor whenever the central processor is prepared to take on a new problem. In this manner, one has a central processor operating at pretty nearly full efficiency; at the other end, one has human users having essentially instantaneous use of the machine. The bottleneck is solved by having a secondary machine serving as a buffer.

Specifically, we propose that all inputs of small and medium problems be fed to the buffer. The buffer would sort these and file them on one of the marvelous new disk memories, known as random access memories. These disks can store several million numbers or instructions and have any block of a thousand numbers available in a fraction of a second. The disks would, in effect, be the filing cabinet in which the buffer stores up the incoming programs and from which the central processor takes the problems one at a time for servicing. In turn, when the problem has been serviced the central processor writes the answer on a disk from where it goes to the buffer and the output typewriters. Storing problems on the disks has an additional tremendous advantage. Namely, if the user finds that a minor correction will fix up his previously incorrect program (a very common experience!), he is not forced to input his entire program again, since this program still exists on a disk. He simply types out the small correction and the machine can insert this correction in the appropriate place in his program, and rerun it.

Since we are convinced that the major deterrent to using high speed computers for research purposes is the time-consuming and frustrating experience of debugging the program, we feel that the above procedure, designed primarily for educational needs, will also be of tremendous use for faculty research.

Any faculty member wishing to use the computer can write the program and debug it at his leisure. If he wishes, he may walk up to one of the 20 typewriters and sit at the typewriter until his problem has been debugged. Or he may work on it a few minutes at a time, knowing that each time he returns to one of the input devices the machine will still remember everything that he had done previously.

While we are not likely to purchase the fastest machine available, it is entirely possible that we will give the fastest service on research in the country. It is true that the actual running time of a given problem may require 5 or 10 hours where a much faster machine might do it in 1 hour. However, including debugging time, our own faculty member will still be able to receive an answer within 24 hours; a faculty member at the institution having a faster machine may require several weeks of debugging before availing himself of the one hour of computing time. The net effect will be that we provide 24 or 48 hour service instead of service spread out over weeks.

Perhaps the best way to evaluate this method of operation is to compare computing centers with a college library. It is hoped that in the future, students will make use of a high speed computer throughout their undergraduate career in the same manner that they now use the library. Not all students use the library, but most of them find it one of their most valuable assets. Some students go to the library only rarely, while some spend a major fraction of their time in the library. Similarly, we may find some students who have no use at all for a high speed computing center, many more students who will use it only occasionally, when specifically required by faculty members, and many students who will find it a valuable tool for their entire undergraduate education.

It is an old controversy in library circles as to whether a library should be open stack or closed stack. It is clear that from the point of view of staff efficiency a closed-stack library is preferable. There is a smaller loss of books, books are misplaced more rarely, and the staff has complete control over all operations inside the stacks. It is equally obvious that from the point of view of the thousands of users, an open stack library is infinitely preferable.

The analogy is perfect. The standard operation of a computing center is that of the closed-stack method, where the users hand in a problem, have to wait a significant amount of time to have it serviced, and have answers handed back to them. They can communicate with the computing machine only through intermediaries. Our proposed solution amounts to an open stack operation of the computing center where users have essentially immediate access to and direct use of the computing machine.

The shortcomings of our system are exactly those of an open-stack library. There will be some loss, in students not making efficient use of the machine. There will be some delays in larger problems, since they will have to wait until small student and debugging runs are serviced. There may be some complaints from the professional staff that a good deal of machine time is being "wasted."

However, from the point of view of the user, we hope that our Center will be a dream installation. He will be able to walk in and make use of the machine at his leisure, without having to explain to anyone why and how he is using the machine. He can return to his problem whenever he wishes, and make as much or as little use of the Center as he alone desires. He will not have costly delays in waiting to receive an answer from the machine, and he is entirely free of red tape. We predict that our Center will become a significant research and educational tool for the vast majority of faculty and students on the campus—a statement that very few other educational institutions can make at the present time.

S